elements of mathematical sociology

elements of
mathematical
sociology

Murray A. Beauchamp
University of Waterloo

RANDOM HOUSE · NEW YORK

301.0184
B38e
77713
Feb. 1972

To Barbara

foreword

to every reader

This is a book about sociology. More particularly, it is a book about the uses of mathematics in sociology. It is not concerned with mathematics per se. Mathematical techniques are developed only so they can be applied to real problems in various fields of social science. Because the emphasis is on application, the development of mathematical ideas is sometimes sketchy, oriented more toward why a particular method is used than toward rigorous proof. This is not to say that rigor is unimportant but that it would be out of place in a book of this kind.

How much mathematics is required to be able to use this book? Formally, not much. What is usually called high school mathematics is enough. Practically all the advanced mathematics that is required, as well as some elementary topics like the use of summation signs, is developed in the book itself. The reader shouldn't worry about his training; he should just go ahead and try mathematics.

Exercises have been inserted throughout the book to enable the reader to test himself. Some are very simple, requiring the reader only to carry the development a step or two forward. Others are quite difficult, occasionally inviting the reader to do what no one else has done before. Answers are not given—sometimes because none are known. Mathematical sociology is a new field, so there is plenty of room for the newcomer to dig in.

to the sociologically sophisticated

Throughout this book, the emphasis is on the application of mathematics to the solution of sociological problems. But sociology being the science it is, not everyone agrees on what the problems are or how they should be formulated. Because I have no way to resolve these difficulties, I have frequently resorted to simplified formulations of various theories in order to show how mathematical techniques can be used, without going into all the very real complexities presented by the original theories.

For example, reference is occasionally made to "functionalism." Every sociologist is aware of the great controversies that have grown up around this topic. Countless articles and many entire books have been devoted to it. I have *not* tried to cover this ground. While these controversies are exciting and important, a discussion of them would only detract from the particular purpose of this book. Whatever his "school," the reader is invited to try to use mathematics in his approach to sociology. I am convinced that the techniques can be useful, no matter what the philosophy of the reader.

to the mathematically sophisticated

In the Preface to his *Pure Mathematics,* G. H. Hardy notes that Littlewood said that the book had the tone of a missionary talking to the cannibals. Much of the present book will sound like that to the mathematician. Most of the mathematics is simple, and quite a bit of space is devoted to the explanation of elementary topics. My teaching experience has been that it is precisely these basic topics that confuse the nonmathematical reader and help convince him that he cannot "do" mathematics. The use of subscripts, for example, is often a total mystery to the uninitiated.

Throughout, the exposition of mathematical ideas is made as simple as possible. Distinctions that are of interest and importance to the mathematician are often glossed over, because I think they would only confuse the sociologically oriented and detract from the main purpose of the text. There is, I believe, nothing mathematically *incorrect* in what follows. But the mathematician may sometimes feel that the discussion is incomplete. For example, I do not distinguish between "mapping into" and "mapping onto." Moreover, the distinction between a "relation" and a "function" is not spelled out, and continuity is never defined.

On the other hand, it does not follow that the mathematics used here is trivial or limited to "freshman" topics. Graph theory, for example, is unknown territory even to many professional mathematicians. Although this book is aimed primarily at sociologists, I hope it may be of some interest to mathematicians. In the past, many mathematical ideas were inspired by the needs of the physical sciences. In the future, the social sciences might well provide equal stimulation. Cooperation between sciences can only be to everyone's benefit.

contents

elements of mathematical sociology

i

some uses of
mathematical sociology

In a widely quoted remark, Bertrand Russell once said that mathematics is a science where we never know what we are talking about. It would seem to follow that a mathematical sociologist is a sociologist who never knows what he is talking about. But since this characteristic may not be sufficient to distinguish him from his colleagues in other fields, we will try to show in this chapter just what *is* characteristic of the approach used by the mathematical sociologist.

mathematical sociology and general sociology

One of the things I hope to do in this volume is to dispel the notion that mathematical sociology is a narrow area of specialization that is of interest only to a small clique of misplaced mathematicians. Rather, I hope to show that "math soc" is relevant to all areas of sociology. Knowledge of some of the techniques presented here could be helpful to many sociologists, whether their interest be in religion, stratification, or role theory. Of course, one can be a specialist in mathematical sociology, just as one can be a specialist in social statistics, but the real justification for mathematics will come if it can help working sociologists do their jobs just a little better.

Poincaré once remarked that sociology was the only science that had a method but no subject. This statement is just true enough to allow us to speak at all about "mathematical sociology," which differs from other areas of sociology not in the substantive phenomena with which it deals but in the way in which it approaches these phenomena. In this chapter we shall illustrate some of the ways in which this mathematical approach can help sociologists in the construction of theory. We shall discuss the formulation of concepts, the formulation of propositions, and the introduction of new concepts.

The mathematics used in this chapter is extremely simple. No assumptions have been made concerning the mathematical training of the reader, so there is nothing in this chapter that should not be understandable even to a reader who has forgotten whatever mathematics he may have learned. However, the inference should not be made that the mathematics in mathematical sociology is *never* complicated or difficult. Sometimes it is; tough problems may require tough methods. But I do hope to suggest that what the mathematical sociologist has to say can be understood by any interested sociologist.

This chapter is entitled *"Some* Uses of Mathematical Sociology." I do not intend to try to cover the field in one chapter or even in this book. The uses to which the mathematical approach have been put are multitudinous.[1] Studies have ranged in topic from the size of groups at cocktail parties to the magnitude of the arms race; from attempts to define "love" to attempts to formalize interaction theories; from changes in consumer brand preferences to changes in the social class system. The uses to which "math soc" *could* be put depend only on our imagination; any a priori boundaries would be completely arbitrary. (Of course, one would suspect that some parts of sociology are likely to be more resistant than others. The application of mathematics to the study of social mobility does not come as a surprise. Personally, I would not expect to see much being done in the sociology of knowledge of the Mannheim sort—at least not in the near future. But I would not be brash enough to say that something could not be done.) The applications of mathematics that are discussed in this chapter are ones that I think are particularly interesting and significant.

formulation of concepts

Every science starts with certain basic concepts—certain ways of viewing the world. Physicists concern themselves with "mass" and "energy," with "velocity" and "acceleration." Every physicist knows that these concepts are not as simple as they sound. He knows that "mass" is easily confused with "weight" and that many years passed before his predecessors clearly distinguished between "force" and "energy." To invent concepts is not difficult; to come up with clear, useful concepts is a long, hard struggle.

Sociology is infamous for its multiplication of terms, its neologisms, and its use of "words no one can understand to say what everyone knows." The history of sociology is strewn with the corpses of loosely used, badly defined terms: "race," "civilization," "progress." The use of mathematics in the formulation of concepts may help us achieve greater clarity for our theories. Of course, the employment of symbols and equations is no guarantee of wisdom; a stupid idea clearly stated is no less stupid. And misunderstanding of the nature of mathematics has led many intelligent scholars down blind alleys. Stuart Dodd fell into the trap of assuming that mathematics is nothing more than a notational system. His book *Dimensions of Society* [2] (extensively cited by Lundberg in his *Foundations of Sociology* [3]) was rightly criticized by both mathematicians and sociologists. Sociologists pointed out that Dodd's system of expressing all societal phenomena in terms of a very few "indicators" lumped most things of interest to sociologists into one category. Mathematicians criticized his shorthand system for not enabling any manipulations to be made to produce new theorems. Kaplan neatly expressed the problem: "Dodd's basic error is his failure to realize that after 'Let x equal such-and-such' the important statement is still to come. The question is how to put *that* statement in mathematical form." [4]

In the quarter century since Dodd's book was published, his system has fallen almost entirely into disuse. Mathematically minded sociologists now are more sophisticated and correspondingly more modest in their ambitions. No one today attempts to express everything with a single "master formula." We will be content if we can put some concepts and some propositions into mathematical form to elucidate some aspects of sociology.

Let us consider one of the most widely used concepts in social science—status. An individual's status is usually defined as his position in a group. The term "position" suggests a spatial image, and since we use "high" and "low" to describe positions in space, a natural question to ask is whether some status is higher or lower than some other. This question is easiest to answer if we are talking about a formal organization (though locations in an informal group may be just as fixed). But even if we have an organization chart before us, if it is anything more complex than a straight descending line of authority, who should be assigned the higher status may not always be apparent. For example, persons on the same level down from the top do not necessarily have equal status.

As a simple example, consider Figure 1.1, an organization chart

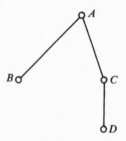

FIGURE 1.1

in which A is the president, B and C are vice-presidents, and D is an office boy. (Lines indicate who reports to whom. Length in inches of any one line is irrelevant.) Clearly A is on top and D is on the bottom, but what about B and C?

To analyze the figure, a simple table—more formally, a matrix—may be constructed in the following manner. Each person's relation to another individual is indicated by a plus sign if he is higher and a minus sign if he is lower. A number is used to indicate how far he is from the other individual in lines of descending authority. For example, we would have the following row for the president:

	A	B	C	D
A	0	$+1$	$+1$	$+2$

This matrix shows that A is "one up" from B and C and "two up" from D. (Of course, he is no distance from himself.) The row for the office boy is:

	A	B	C	D
D	−2	0	−1	0

He is two down from the president and one down from C, but he is not in any line of descending authority from B. The rows for B and C are:

	A	B	C	D
B	−1	0	0	0
C	−1	0	0	+1

Putting this all together, the matrix is:

	A	B	C	D
A	0	+1	+1	+2
B	−1	0	0	0
C	−1	0	0	+1
D	−2	0	−1	0

We now use the matrix to define "relative status" by a very simple operation: A person's relative status is the sum of the entries in the row corresponding to his name. The row corresponding to A adds up to $+4$, the row corresponding to D adds up to -3. The sum of the B row is -1, whereas C has a sum of 0. Since 0 is less than $+4$ but greater than -1 or -3, C has the second highest status, B is third, and D is fourth. The relative positions of B and C go along with the common-sense judgment that a person with subordinates has higher status than a person without subordinates, and the more subordinates one has the higher one's status, other things being equal.

The reader may object that the phrase "other things being equal" is terribly restrictive, making the method inapplicable to many interesting situations. A technical expert (perhaps a corporation lawyer) might be the same level down from the boss as a vice-president in charge of production; the latter may have many subordinates, the former few or none. Yet the expert's paycheck may be larger than the vice-president's. Very well then; let us reformulate the organization chart. Perhaps we could use a line to mean that A's decisions determine B's behavior. We can still use the matrix to analyze the resulting chart. The main concern here is not to determine the best way of drawing charts—that can be determined only through trial and error. The point is that such a chart can be used to assign an unambiguous relative status to everyone concerned.

Is the matrix anything more than a shorthand, a different way of writing the organization chart? (After all, it contains no information that is not already present in the chart.) Without being able to justify it here, I'll say "yes." In the next chapter we will look at graph theory and matrix algebra, and the fact that the matrix used here fits into a developed body of theory will become clear; the matrix can be manipulated to produce new theorems about organizations. For some examples, the reader is referred to an article by Frank Harary (from which this method—slightly altered—is taken), in which new theorems are produced.[5]

formulating propositions

Good concepts, clearly formulated, are essential to science, but they are the beginning, not the end, of investigation. Too many sociologists (and other scientists) think they have solved a problem when they have named a phenomenon. But calling names often only indicates that you have lost your temper. The real business of science is the formulation of empirically testable propositions. In this context, the manipulative aspects of mathematics make that science especially useful. By playing with formulas we can often uncover unexpected connections between concepts.

To illustrate how such manipulation is done within the bounds of an introductory chapter (assuming no mathematical background on the part of the reader), I am going to simplify radically some rather complicated relationships. Such simplification does not necessarily indicate a weakness; if our model reveals some interesting new relationships we can "complicate it up" later.

In his investigation of anomic suicide, Durkheim came to the conclusion that there was a negative relationship between group cohesion and deviant behavior: the greater the group cohesion, the less the deviant behavior engaged in by members of the group.[6] He did not claim that the relation was exactly proportional. He would not have said, for instance, that whenever group cohesion increased by 3 units, the rate of deviant behavior decreased by 6 units. But I am going to make just such an assumption; if it makes you feel queasy remember that it has been consciously made. This being done, we can write Durkheim's finding in a formula. We will use D to indicate deviant behavior and G to indicate group cohesion. The formula is:

$$D = -kG + h$$

where k and h are constants whose value would have to be determined empirically. (Of course k must be positive.) Suppose that k equals 3 and h equals 20. The equation would be

$$D = -3G + 20$$

If G were equal to 1, D would be equal to 17; if G were equal to 2, D would equal 14 and so on.

In a well-known paper, Robert Merton approached deviant behavior from a structural point of view.[7] A social group sets up certain goals for all its members (e.g. wealth); and prescribes certain accepted ways of attaining these goals. (Wealth, for example, may be obtained by inheritance or hard work.) But some members may be unable to attain the goals by the prescribed means. (Some members of minority groups, for example, may not be able to obtain wealth no matter how hard they work.) In such a case, the "deprived" persons may resort to other, deviant means, stealing, for example. Merton suggested that deviant behavior may be negatively related to the degree of access to normatively approved means of attaining group-defined goals. Calling this degree of access A, using D as before, to represent deviant behavior, and making assumptions like those in the first example, we can write Merton's idea like this:

$$D = -KA + b$$

where K and b are to be determined empirically. (K is positive.)

Now K and b are not necessarily the same as the k and h in the Durkheim equation, but D is the same in both cases. Thus:

$$-kG + h = -KA + b$$

Subtracting h from both sides gives us

$$-kG = -KA + b - h$$

and dividing through with $-k$ we end up with

$$G = \frac{K}{k} A + \frac{(h - b)}{k}$$

This equation is rather clumsy, so let us make $K/k = c$ and $(h - b)/k = d$. Our equation now is

$$G = cA + d$$

which we can read as: "Group cohesion is proportional to the degree of access to normatively approved means of attaining group-defined goals."

As far as I know this relationship has never been noticed before. It suggests a structural aspect of group cohesion. This aspect is significant, for it suggests new interpretations of old facts. For example, most would agree that Catholics have greater cohesion than Protestants. Is the widespread use of "indulgences" a means of "access" open to Catholics but not to Protestants? It is tempting to think so. Of course, we would want independent means of measuring G and A. And the proposition does not mean that nothing else is involved in group cohesion, any more than Merton would claim that nothing else was involved in deviant behavior.

The equation is not complete as it stands; no limits are indicated. Yet surely there must be upper and lower limits of group cohesion. This is no disaster—in physics, Hooke's law states that the elongation in a spring is proportional to the force with which the spring is pulled. But the fact that the spring will break if the force is too great is hardly a refutation of Hooke. (Some physicists are fond of saying that Hooke's law is valid over the entire range to which it applies.) The point here is that from two well-known (albeit slightly altered) propositions, a third proposition has been produced by simple manipulation.

formulating new concepts

Much of this work will be concerned with translating well-known sociological concepts and propositions into mathematical form for various purposes. I think this is a very important task, introducing a degree of precision of statement into a notably imprecise discipline. Herbert Simon, who has done groundbreaking work along these lines, claims that his "mere translations" not only express the meaning of the original statements but express it better.[8] (In a later chapter we will look at Simon's translations of Homans.) But there is another aspect

FIGURE 1.2

of mathematical sociology: some concepts can receive satisfactory expression *only* in mathematics. For example, the difficulty of expressing any but the most elementary statistical ideas without using mathematical symbolism is well known to every statistics teacher (and student).

The example that is used here is more abstract than statistics. Social psychologists are interested in communication: its content, effectiveness, diffusion and so on. A common type of experiment in this field consists of giving a problem to the members of a group and asking them to solve it by communicating with each other over some kind of network. Leavitt, in one of the first such experiments,[9] gave the participants parts of a puzzle that could be solved only by finding out what parts were held by the other participants. He wanted to find out how various patterns of communication affected the subjects' ability to solve the problem.

For simplicity, let us assume that the participants communicate by telephone. The lines could be hooked up in various ways. If there were four subjects the phones might be connected in a "chain," as in Figure 1.2, or in a "T" formation, as in Figure 1.3. The reader can easily think of other patterns. Notice that the chain and the T have the same number of lines; they are just arranged differently.

We would like to see how the layout of communication channels affects problem-solving efficiency. "Efficiency" is fairly easy to measure: we can time the group, see how many mistakes were made and so on. But how do we measure the "pattern" of a communication network?

In a well-known paper, published in 1950, Bavelas suggested a measure of "centrality" to characterize a network.[10] His index had certain deficiencies, which I corrected in a later paper.[11] This improved index will be used in the subsequent discussion.

One thing that changes when a pattern is changed is the distance between participants. By "distance" in this context we mean the number of telephone lines linking two people. In the chain, if A wants

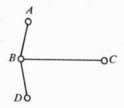

FIGURE 1.3

to pass a message to D he must give it to B, who gives it to C, who passes it along to D. In the chain, the distance from A to D is 3. In the T formation, A gives his message to B, who gives it directly to D. The distance here is only 2.

We can use this distance to characterize each member of the group in terms of his distance from others. In the chain, A is 1 step from B, 2 steps from C, and 3 steps from D, so A's total distance from others is $1 + 2 + 3 = 6$. In the same network, B is distance 1 from A and from C and distance 2 from D, so his distance is $1 + 1 + 2 = 4$. (It should be obvious that in this pattern, C has the same distance as B, and D has the same as A.)

Now we would like a measure of centrality that would be low when a person's distance from others is large and high when his distance from others is small. So, instead of using distance from others, we will use the inverse of distance. In the chain the distance measure for A is $1/6$ and for B is $1/4$. Distance in a network, of course, depends on the number of other persons. Using d for distance from others and n for the number of participants, we define "relative centrality" of a participant as $RC = (n - 1)/d$. The useful property of this index is that for a participant who is in direct touch with every other participant, the highest value of the index is 1. Thus the relative centrality of A is $3/6 = 1/2$; the relative centrality of B is $3/4$. Obviously, B is in a more central position than A.

Using the symmetry of A and D and of B and C, we can chart the relative centralities of the members of the chain:

Relative centrality of $A = .5$
Relative centrality of $B = .75$
Relative centrality of $C = .75$
Relative centrality of $D = .5$

These add up to 2.5. Because there are 4 participants, we can find the average relative centrality of the chain simply by dividing:

$$\frac{2.5}{4} = .62$$

Now let us do the same for the members of the T network. Person A is distance 1 from B, 2 from C, and 2 from D, his relative centrality is $3/5$. By symmetry we see that C and D will be the same. But B is distance 1 from each of the others, so his relative centrality is $3/3 = 1$. Adding up these figures we get 2.8. Dividing by 4 we get an average relative centrality of .7. This figure tells us that the chain is less centralized than the T, which would seem to agree with intuition.

We can use average relative centrality to characterize a pattern. It is a simple matter to show that in a network where all participants can communicate directly with each other, the average centrality is 1. Where such communication is not possible, the index is less than 1. Notice that in computing the average relative centrality we also characterized different positions in the pattern. In the T, person B has a strategic position, indicated by his high centrality index. No one in the chain has a comparable position.

The basic idea of centrality is quite simple, though the mathematical formulation can get rather complicated. But this concept would be almost impossible to formulate without mathematics. Verbal expressions (like "chain" or "wheel") are so imprecise as to be unusable.

13

Formulation of such an index can be the most distinctive contribution of mathematical sociology.

conclusion

After reading this chapter some individuals might jump to the conclusion that a mathematical sociologist is just another sociologist doing his job, differing from his colleagues only in the technique he uses to analyze his data. This conclusion would be correct. Some of his techniques are simple, like the ones used in this chapter. Others are rather more complex; they will be discussed in subsequent chapters. Some are quite complicated and are beyond the scope of this book.

In principle, the problems tackled by the mathematical sociologist are the same problems that nonmathematical sociologists tackle. No doubt there is a degree of methodological selectivity—that is, scientists are likely to choose problems with which they can cope by using the methodological tools they happen to possess. But this tendency is countered by a curiosity to see what the tools can do. Abraham Kaplan calls this the "principle of the little boy with the hammer"—everything he comes across needs hammering. If the reader thinks he may be able to use the hammer of mathematical sociology to straighten out some wrinkly problem, he is invited to proceed to the next chapter.

EXERCISES—CHAPTER I

1a. Look at Figure 1.4. In organization chart, who has the higher status, B or C? (Note that both have the same number of subordi-

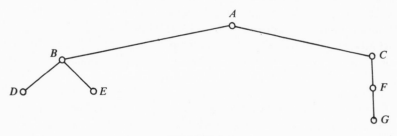

FIGURE 1.4

nates.) First decide on intuitive grounds, then try the matrix method. Do they agree? If not, which is better?

1b. Sometimes you may want to compare two organizations, but one has more members than the others. As given, the matrix method is not very satisfactory for this case. Devise an index that will give better comparable measures in different size groups.

For example, look at Figures 1.5 and 1.6.

| **FIGURE 1.5** | **FIGURE 1.6** |

In Figure 1.5, A has relative status $1 + 2 + 2 = 5$. In Figure 1.6, A has relative status $1 + 1 + 2 + 2 + 2 = 8$. Can you arrange the formula so that A has the same index in both organizations?

2. In the article cited in the text, Merton presents a table of modes of adaptation, based on different combinations of "means" and "ends." Harary has expanded this table to include all possible combinations. You might look at his article for another illustration of the use of very simple mathematics to extend a sociological concept.[12]

Can you relate group cohesion to the different modes of adaptation? Perhaps there are different kinds of "access." Or you might approach the problem from the other direction: by determining the "blockages" to the normatively approved means of attaining goals.

3. Centrality can be applied to other patterns besides communication networks. If you draw a sociogram, in which a line between two points indicates that two people interact, you can measure centrality in the same way as was done for the communication network. Such a finding should not surprise us since communication and interaction are so closely connected. What does knowing the centrality of a sociogram of a group tell us about it?

NOTES

1. A very comprehensive, cross-referenced bibliography is being prepared by R. Paris-Steffens, N. Katz, W. McPhee, and E. Rose: *Formal Theory in the Behavioral Sciences: A Bibliography,* Publication Number 78 (Boulder: University of Colorado, Institute of Behavioral Sciences).

2. Stuart Dodd, *Dimensions of Society* (New York: Macmillan, 1942). In all fairness it should be mentioned that Dodd has done very good work on the diffusion of information. There is no place I know where you can get a concise summary of "S-Theory"; you might look at some of the reviews it got when it was published. And of course you can look at the book itself.

3. G. Lundberg, *Foundations of Sociology* (New York: Macmillan, 1939). Actually, Lundberg was endorsing the attempt to use mathematics in sociology more than he was endorsing Dodd's particular system.

4. A. Kaplan, "Sociology Learns the Language of Mathematics," in *Commentary,* 14 (1952), 274–284. Worth reading in its entirety.

5. Frank Harary, "Status and Contrastatus," in *Sociometry,* 22 (March 1959), 23–43.

6. Émile Durkheim, *Suicide* (1897).

7. Robert Merton, *Social Theory and Social Structure* (New York: Free Press, 1949), chap. 4.

8. Herbert Simon, *Models of Man* (New York: Wiley, 1957), p. 89.

9. H. Leavitt, *Some Effects of Certain Communication Patterns on Group Performance* (Ph.D. Dissertation, Massachusetts Institute of Technology, 1949).

10. A. Bavelas, "Communication Patterns in Task Oriented Groups," in *Journal of the Acoustical Society of America* (1950), pp. 271–282.

11. Murray Beauchamp, "An Improved Index of Centrality," in *Behavioral Science,* 10, No. 2 (April 1965), 161–163.

12. Frank Harary, "Merton Revisited: A New Classification for Deviant Behavior," in *American Sociological Review,* 31, No. 5 (October 1966), 693–697.

ii

sets and graphs

Willard Gibbs, the greatest mathematical physicist America has ever produced, was normally a rather quiet man. But one day, listening to his colleagues at Yale debating the relative merits of "languages" and "mathematics," he got to his feet and declared with considerable force: "But mathematics *is* a language!" Gibbs' special interest was in vector mathematics, which can be considered as a language for physics. In this chapter we will present the theory of sets and graphs that seems to be a very good language for sociology.

sets and subsets

One of the most important scientific developments in the past half century has been the evolution of the theory of sets. Today set theory forms the foundation of all mathematics. We will be interested in it both for direct application to sociology and as a language that will unite the mathematical theories we touch on later.

17

A set is a collection of objects, distinguishable from each other and usually referred to as the "elements" of the set. The elements may be almost anything. In mathematics they might be odd numbers, complex numbers, lines, points, or solids. In sociology they might be people, cities, statuses, or beliefs. A set may contain 5 elements or 5,000, or it might have an infinite number of elements. It might even have no elements at all, in which case we refer to it as the "empty" set.

(In mathematics, indiscriminate use of the concepts "set" and "set membership" can result in paradoxes. Some of these are rather amusing. For a readable account see Kasner and Newman, *Mathematics and the Imagination.* However, such problems are unlikely to trouble us in applying set theory to sociology.)

If we have a set with elements x_1, x_2, x_3. . . . x_n, we usually write $X = \{x\}$ and refer to some member of it as x_i. To indicate that a particular x is a member of X we write $x \,\epsilon\, X$. To indicate that, say, y is not a member of X, we write $y \,\epsilon\, X$. Suppose that X is the set of all even numbers. Then $2 \,\epsilon\, X$ and $3 \,\epsilon\, X$.

Suppose we have a set R of all residents of the United States. Obviously, this set is composed of two sets: F, the set of all female residents, and M, the set of all male residents. F and M are referred to as subsets of R. Notice that if $x \,\epsilon\, F$, then necessarily $x \,\epsilon\, R$. (The reverse is not necessarily true: $x \,\epsilon\, R$ does not imply $x \,\epsilon\, F$.) This is a distinguishing characteristic of subsets, so let us state it formally. If we have two sets, X and Y, such that $p \,\epsilon\, X$ implies $p \,\epsilon\, Y$, then we say that X is a subset of Y. (It follows that any set is a subset of itself. We shall see that this is convenient terminology.)

Since every subset is also a set, there is no reason why it cannot in turn be broken down into subsets; conversely, any set can be thought of as a subset of some more inclusive set. For example, consider G, the set of all students at the University of Guelph in 1968. There is a subset S of G, consisting of all sociology majors at Guelph that year, and S has a subset F consisting of all foreign students majoring in sociology. Going the other way, G may be thought of as a subset of all college students in Canada, which, in turn, may be thought of as a subset of all college students in North America and so on.

An element may be a member of more than one set at a time. Using the sets above and a set W of all women, we can find girls who are members of both G and W—in other words, college women at Guelph. All girls who are members of both W and G form a set called the intersection of W and G, written $W \cap G$. We can form another set, consisting of all persons who are either women or students at Guelph or both; this new set is called the union and is written $W \cup G$.

functions

One concept is so fundamental in mathematics that it has popped up time and time again, in different areas and under different names: function, correspondence, mapping, transformation, and more. Basically this concept concerns a relation between two sets. If the elements of one set are matched individually to elements in the other set, we talk of a "correspondence" between the sets. If the configuration of one set is the same as the other, then it seems natural to talk of a "mapping" of one onto the other. If one set can be changed into the other by some operation, then "transformation" would be proper. The most inclusive word is "function." To say that Y is a function of X means we have a rule by which every element of X is related to some element of Y.

We are all familiar with the concept of function, whether we are familiar with the terminology or not. Suppose we claim that our car gets 20 miles to the gallon. Then we could say that gasoline consumption is a function of distance traveled. If we call x the number of miles and y the number of gallons of gas consumed, we could write $y = x/20$. Putting this relationship in the language of sets, we can set up a table listing different values of x and the corresponding value of y. Thus:

Y	X
1	20
2	40
3	60
4	80
5	100

The numbers in the first column are from the set Y; the numbers in the second column are from the set X.

Sometimes a complete representation of a function can be given simply by listing the elements of one set in one column and the corresponding elements of the other set in a second column. But in most cases, including our simple example, this representation is not practical or even possible. We have listed the elements of Y that correspond to values from X of $x = 20$, $x = 40$, $x = 60$, $x = 80$ and $x = 100$, but certainly the mileage on a trip need not be one of these numbers. A more complete table would include $x = 20.1$, $x = 20.2$, $x = 20.15$ and so on. Clearly a table would be out of the question. But we don't need the table, because we have the rule $y = x/20$, which enables us to calculate the corresponding value of y for any x we happen to be interested in.

Sometimes we do not even have to know what the rule is, as long as we at least know that there *is* such a rule. In such a case (which we will illustrate in a moment), functional notation is a very convenient tool. To denote that there is a rule relating X to Y we write $y = f(x)$, which we read as "y is a function of x" or "y equals f of x." The letter f is not sacred: we could equally well write "$y = g(x)$" or "$y = F(x)$." Of course it is important to be consistent. If we write $y = f(x)$ and then later write $y = g(x)$, the reader must assume that the different letters represent different functions. For example, $y = f(x)$ might indicate the relation between mileage and gas consumption for a Volkswagen, and $y = g(x)$ might indicate the relation for a Rolls-Royce—presumably a different function. (It is very important to understand that $f(x)$ does *not* mean "f times x"; f indicates a function, not a number.)

An interesting use of the function concept was made by Herbert Simon.[1] Some critics of social science have contended that there is a basic weakness in studying people. If we make a prediction and let the people involved know about it, they can change their behavior and thus falsify the prediction. Simon did not believe that the possibility of falsification necessarily followed, so he set up a mathematical model.

Let us take a simple case, where we are trying to predict what percent of the vote some particular candidate (call him A) is going to get in a forthcoming election. Suppose we gather data in the usual manner—public opinion polls and so on. Now we are going to make the assumption that publishing our results will influence people's choices. If we say that A is going to get 5 percent of the vote, some people may vote for him out of sympathy—the so-called underdog effect. (Something like this effect may have partially accounted for the

Truman victory in 1948.) On the other hand, prediction of a sweep may induce some people to vote for a winner—this is the "bandwagon effect" (which may account for some landslide victories, such as Johnson's in 1964). Whatever the exact relation may be, we assume there *is* a relation between the prediction and the decision to cast a vote. Let us call the published prediction x and the actual result of the election y; then $y = f(x)$. Both x and y can take on values ranging from 0 percent to 100 percent. Figure 2.1, in which a hypothetical line represents $f(x)$, may clarify what we are doing.

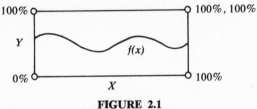

FIGURE 2.1

To calculate what vote will follow from any given prediction, we look at the particular value of X to see where it crosses $f(x)$ and read the corresponding value of y from the vertical line.

We do not know what the actual "shape" of $f(x)$ is, but we can make the following two assumptions about it:

1. For every possible prediction, x, there is exactly one outcome, y.
2. The line representing the function is continuous. This continuity would take a long time to define rigorously; here we will just say that the line we drew has no "breaks" or "jumps." We will see shortly why this condition is very important.

Now let us draw in the figure a line representing the function $y = x$. (This function, of course, means that for any x the corresponding value of y is numerically exactly equal.) It can be proved rigorously (the "fixed point" theorem) and should be obvious intuitively, that this line must cross the first line at some point. What should also be clear is that if the two lines meet at point P, then $f(x) = y = x$ at that point. In other words, if we were to publish that prediction, it would be exactly correct.

Exercise: What happens if the lines representing $f(x)$ and $y = x$ cross at more than one point? For that matter, what if $f(x)$ is just $y = x$?

The above may, at first reading, sound more like legerdemain than logic, but it is not. The logic is inescapable. In principle, it is always possible to publish a prediction that will be correct—if the assumptions made above are correct. The "self-falsifying" aspect of social science disappears.

The phrase "in principle" is quite important. We assume that $f(x)$ exists, but that does not mean we know how to construct this line. Indeed, this operation could be very difficult, though I know of no reason why this should be impossible. But remember: the problem was not to show how to make a correct prediction, but just to show that publication will not falsify it.

The whole burden of Simon's argument rests on assumptions 1 and 2. The first assumption is not particularly troublesome; it seems reasonable that different values of x will give different values of y. Even if the assumption were false, we could publish all values of y for that particular x. But the second assumption is a little more difficult to swallow. Let us see why it is necessary. If $f(x)$ is not continuous, we conceivably could have a situation similar to that shown in Figure 2.2.

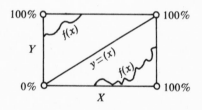

FIGURE 2.2

The diagonal line goes through the "gap" and thus never crosses $f(x)$, so *no* published prediction could be correct.

There is no sociological reason to think that $f(x)$ would have a big hole in it, but equally there is no sociological reason to think that it would not. Yet the assumption of continuity is essential to the argument. (Even a small hole would destroy it.) So the question: is a prediction in social science necessarily self-falsifying? is not answered in any absolute sense. But far from feeling defeated, the mathematical sociologist can claim a victory; Simon's formulation has shown exactly which assumptions are necessary to answer the question. The whole issue has been changed from a situation of vague verbal argument to a technical question about the nature of the function.

functions as mappings

Functions are very commonly used by applied mathematicians to express the manner in which one variable changes as another is varied. A physicist is interested in the way electrical resistance changes as temperature is varied, an economist is interested in the relation between price and demand, and a psychologist may want to know how recall improves as the number of repetitions increases. Sociologists deal with some functional relationships, the variation of family size with family income, for example. (Is it too heavy handed for the author to note that "function" in the mathematical sense is quite different from "function" in the sociological sense? The two words may be related in some contexts, but it is best right now to think of them as homonyms!)

Many sociologists, such as George Homans,[2] look forward to the day when more sociological propositions will be expressed as functions. These functions will take the following general form: Some attribute of a group or individual changes if some other attribute changes. We write this function $y = f(x)$. The notation implies nothing about causality; it cannot distinguish between "y causes x," "x causes y," and "x and y are both caused by z." The letters x and y need not represent quantities, but they must vary. In the simplest case, x might take the values x_1 and x_2 and y might take the values y_1 and y_2. The corresponding relations would be $y_1 = f(x_1)$ and $y_2 = f(x_2)$. The relation need not be deterministic; f might simply indicate the probability that a particular value of y is associated with a particular value of x.

A somewhat different aspect of the "function" concept is brought out when we think of it as "mapping." (Of course from a mathematical point of view, a function and mapping are the same; only our imagery is different.) Instead of thinking of x varying, we think of the set X as a whole and try to relate each element in it to elements in Y. The notation remains the same: $y = f(x)$. John Kemeny gives an excellent illustration of this use.[3] Take a set X of individuals. Each x has a father; call the set of fathers Y. Then $y = f(x)$ can be read "y is the father of x." Note that every person in Y also has a father, say, z. We could write $z = g(y)$ to indicate that "z is the father of y." But this y is the same one that appeared in the previous expression, so we can substitute it there to get $z = g(f(x))$, or simply $z = gf(x)$, which we read "z is the grandfather of x." The two mappings, g and f, joined together like this are called a composite mapping.

Mapping provides a convenient way of comparing structures, particularly when we ask if two sets have the same structure. "Structure" is perhaps the most frequently used and the least frequently defined term in sociology. We will not try here to consider all the ways it is used; for a good review of usages of the more specific term "social structure," see T. B. Bottomore.[4] In the abstract, we can define the structure of a set as its decomposition into subsets. Of course, this decomposition can almost always be carried out in more than one way, so it would be better to say that some set has structures, each one defined by some criteria.

Let us assume that we have two sets, X and Y, each with defined subsets, and some mapping, $y = f(x)$. This mapping relates each member of X to some member of Y. (There is nothing in this to prohibit two elements of X from being mapped into the same element of Y. To go back to Kemeny's example, two or more persons can have the same father.) It might map x_1, say, into y_1. Then this last, y_1, or its equivalent $f(x_1)$, is called the image of x_1.

We will say that X and Y have the same structure if the following statements hold:

1. If x_i and x_j are in the same subset of X, then y_i and y_j are in the same subset of Y.
2. If x_i and x_k are in different subsets of X, then y_i and y_k are in different subsets of Y.

In other words, two sets have the same structure if the distribution of the x's over X and the distribution of the images of the x's over Y are the same.

If for each x there is exactly one y, and for each y exactly one x, then we say that X and Y are isomorphic and that the mapping f is an isomorphism. If they have the same structure by the definition given but do not enjoy this one-to-one correspondence, then we say that X and Y are homomorphic and that the mapping is a homomorphism. Notice that in using this definition of "same structure," we do not have to know what the subsets of X and Y are nor how the x's and y's are distributed; we only have to have some way of knowing if two elements are in the same subset.

Let us see how these concepts can be used in an investigation related to the theory of "status congruence" in sociology. We will set up a model from the theory, then show how the model can be used to analyze some actual data. By a model we simply mean some system of mathematical symbols set up to operate in such a way as to represent an aspect of social phenomena. If our model actually represents what it purports to represent, then manipulation of the symbols under the rules of the system should yield statements that can be translated into true propositions about the phenomena.

(The correspondence between the model and reality is seldom exact. Our empirical data are not always in the form assumed by the model. Sociological data is notoriously "crude," and therefore our approximations to reality may be quite rough. But the construction of the model is nevertheless useful. If our results are too inaccurate, we refine the model or create a new one—at least we know then what the correct model isn't. For a useful discussion of models in physics, see Mary Hesse, *Forces and Fields*.[5] She is interested in Bohr's model of the atom, recognized today as a very rough approximation but still tremendously useful. What she has to say has direct relevance to sociology today.)

A currently popular theory, with application to the analysis of social change, employs the concept of "status congruence," introduced by Lenski.[6] There are many different interpretations of this concept. One such interpretation can be stated as follows: An individual in society has many different statuses—political, economic, educational and so on. In a stable situation, most people find their statuses to be congruent. For example, people with high economic power tend to have considerable political power and vice versa, whereas people low on the economic ladder usually have little political power. Of course there are problems in this formulation. For example, how much political power is "appropriate" to a person of a given economic position?

A dynamic element is introduced when some persons find that their statuses are not congruent. Such people may be motivated to seek balance by causing social change to occur. James Geschwender [7] has suggested an interesting application. Negroes in the United States have generally been poor and have had little power; indeed they have frequently been denied the ballot. But until recently little concerted effort has been made to remedy the situation. The placidity of the Negro masses might be ascribed to the fact that though they perceived their situation to be unpleasant, they also perceived it as congruent. They were poor; thus they were powerless. (Obviously many assumptions of a psychological nature are being made here; though they are important, we will not analyze all the problems associated with them in this book.) But since World War II, and even more since the Korean conflict, when Negroes were able to enter many industrial occupations, their economic status has been bettered—but their political status has not. Thus they perceived incongruence and were motivated to engage in massive political action—the so-called Negro Revolution.

But how do we measure incongruence? One way that avoids many difficulties is to measure it indirectly. We can see how economic status has changed and we can see how political status has changed. If they have not changed in the same way, we can infer that there must be incongruence. We will demonstrate this method, using economic status and educational status—partly because we have data on education but not on political status, and partly because we suspect that discrimination may produce incongruence between educational and economic status. (Negroes frequently complain that they are denied jobs for which they have educational qualifications.)

Census data (for a given year) divides the population of an area into income groupings (how many people have incomes from $1,000 to $1,999 and how many have incomes from $2,000 to $2,999, etc.) and educational attainment groupings (how many people had 1 to 3 years of high school and how many completed high school). Let us call these groupings income brackets and education brackets, respectively.

Let us translate the above into set theory. Consider the set of all incomes (for some specified area or areas) reported in the census of 1950; call this set $I = \{i\}$. Thus i_1 might be the income of Joe Doakes, i_2 the income of John Doe, i_3 the income of Sam Spade. (Of course the census doesn't tell us whose income it is, nor does it report everybody's income, but we are not concerned about that right now.) Next, consider the set of all educational attainments for the same population, for 1950; call it $E = \{e\}$. So e_1 is the educational attainment of Mr. Doakes, e_2 the educational attainment of Mr. Doe, and e_3 the educational attainment of Mr. Spade. Using these terms, a strict definition of status congruence would be: The population under consideration has status congruence only if I is isomorphic to E. This means that if we break I into subsets and E into subsets, then:

1. If i_1 and i_2 are in the same subset of I, then e_1 and e_2 are in the same subset of E;
2. If i_1 and i_3 are in different subsets of I, then e_1 and e_3 are in different subsets of E.

In words, if two people have the same income they should have the same education; if two people have different incomes they should have different educations.

This definition of status congruence is fine for our model but it is going to get us into trouble with our data. The only convenient way we have of breaking down E and I into subsets is to use the income brackets and education brackets given by the census. But these *brackets* are not necessarily identical with the *subsets* assumed by the definition of isomorphism. The brackets are completely arbitrary divisions of the data and may actually obscure the relation between I and E.

Suppose, for example, that Joe Doakes makes $5,000 a year and has completed one year of high school, whereas Sam Spade makes $6,000 a year and has completed three years of high school. Joe and Sam are in different income brackets and different subsets of I. But although they are really in different subsets of E (i.e., we could break E into subsets this way), they are in the same education brackets, simply by virtue of the fact that that is the way the Bureau of the Census lists education. So although E and I can really be isomorphic, this quality would be obscured by our use of brackets as subsets.

But we ought not despair of our model—at least not yet. We may still be in a position to see how E and I change, and thus we may be able to infer a change in congruence. The structures E and I were defined for 1950. Let us look at the income and education structure in 1960; we will call the income and education sets for that year I' and E' respectively. We can write the mapping of I onto E as $e = f(i)$

27

and the mapping of I' onto E' as $e' = g(i')$. Our question is then: Is f the same as g? Clearly if we could show that both f and g were isomorphisms, we could answer positively; if we could show that f was an isomorphism and g was not, we could answer the question in the negative. For the reason given, however, we cannot determine isomorphism. But perhaps we can manipulate our model to give us a question we can answer.

Look at the problem from a different aspect. Sets I and I' are different sets. There must be some mapping, F, that maps one into the other; write this $i' = F(i)$. Similarly, there is a mapping, G, from E to E'; write this $e' = G(e)$. Let us arrange the equations we have thus far:

$$e = f(i) \tag{1}$$

$$e' = g(i') \tag{2}$$

$$i' = F(i) \tag{3}$$

$$e' = G(e) \tag{4}$$

Substituting (1) into (4) we get

$$e' = G(f(i)) = Gf(i) \tag{5}$$

Substituting (3) into (2) we get

$$e' = g(F(i)) = gF(i) \tag{6}$$

Then by setting $e' = e'$ we come up with

$$Gf(i) = gF(i) \tag{7}$$

This last equation tells us that the composite mapping Gf is the same as the composite mapping gF. And with certain technical assumptions (that the mappings have inverses, which is quite reasonable), this tells us that, if F and G are the same, then f and g are the same (technically, they are similar); if F and G are different (nonsimilar), then f and g are different. Verbally, we can interpret this statement to mean that if income structure changed in the same way that educational structure changed, then the relationship between education and income was the same in 1960 as it was in 1950. What we need now is a way to determine if F and G are the same. In other words, we must determine whether F does the same thing to income that G does to education.

homogeneity measurement

What is it that F and G do to I and E? Consider I, the income structure in 1950. It consists of elements distributed in a particular way over the subsets. Similarly, I' consists of a distribution, generally different from I. There are a number of ways in which we can characterize distributions. One way that has certain technical advantages is to measure the "homogeneity."

A set is totally homogeneous with respect to some attribute if all its elements are in one category. For example, a population is homogeneous with respect to income if all its members have the same income. Therefore, a set is less homogeneous (or more heterogeneous) to the extent that its elements are in more than one category and to the extent that they are evenly distributed over the categories. Suppose we have 3 sets, A, B, and C, each with 10 elements. In set A all the elements are in one category; in set B there are 9 elements in one category and 1 element in another; in set C there are 5 elements in one category and 5 in another. Then set A is the most homogeneous and set C is the most heterogeneous. Let us formalize this finding in an index.

Consider a set of n elements. Let X_i be the number of elements in category i. By definition, $\Sigma X_i = n$. (The number of categories is irrelevant but is assumed to be 2 or more.) We will take as our index

$$H = \frac{\Sigma X_i^2}{(\Sigma Xi)^2}$$

First, suppose all the elements are in a single category. Then $\Sigma X^2 = (\Sigma X)^2$ and $H = 1$. This indicates that the set is completely homogeneous. Second, suppose 9/10 of the elements are in category 1 and 1/10 are in category 2. Then $X_1 = 9n/10$ and $X_2 = n/10$, so $X_1 = 9X_2$. Therefore, $\Sigma X^2 = X_1^2 + X_2^2 = (9X_2)^2 + X_2^2 = 82X_2^2$. But $(\Sigma X)^2 =$

$(X_1 + X_2)^2 = (9X_2 + X_2)^2 = 100X_2^2$. So $H = 82/100 = .82$. Finally, suppose half the elements are in one category and half are in the other. Then $X_1 = X_2$, and $\Sigma X^2 = X_1^2 + X_2^2 = 2X_2^2$, and $(\Sigma X)^2 = (2X_2)^2 = 4X_2^2$, so that $H = 2/4 = .5$.

More generally, if the elements are distributed into more than one category, ΣX^2 is smaller than $(\Sigma X)^2$ and thus H is less than 1. By using calculus, it is possible to show that H attains its minimum value when the elements are distributed equally throughout the categories.

Exercise: What is the lowest possible value for H for any given set of n elements? (This exercise requires only algebra, no calculus.)

To apply this index to our problem, we can construct homogeneity indexes for E, I, E' and I'. Let us call these indexes H_e, H_i, H_e' and H_i',

TABLE 1. Homogeneity Indexes for Negro Population of Selected Census Tracts: Cleveland, Ohio, 1950 and 1960

Census Tract	INCOME		EDUCATION	
	1950	1960	1950	1960
S1	.206	.139	.160	.197
S2	.218	.127	.190	.178
S7	.186	.180	.216	.126
S8	.182	.136	.180	.175
T1	.243	.128	.178	.248
T7	.232	.149	.182	.174
V2	.214	.147	.184	.172
X4	.212	.159	.194	.197

respectively. The question we were asking can now be phrased: Is H_i transformed into H_i' in the same way that H_e is transformed into H_e'?

The data presented are intended to be illustrative, because the sample was not randomly drawn. But it is sufficient to show how the method can be used. Eight census tracts were selected from Cleveland, Ohio. They were chosen because the census reported separately the characteristics of the Negro population in 1950 and 1960. The four homogeneity indexes are reported in Table 1.

All tracts show a decrease in income homogeneity from 1950 to

1960. Tracts $S1$, $T1$, and $X4$ show an increase in educational homogeneity; all other tracts show a decrease.

Examination of Table 1 reveals that income homogeneity was decreasing in all tracts at the same time, while education homogeneity was changing in a random manner. Hence the conclusion that the two indexes were not transformed in the same way.

Exercise 1: Because the census tracts were not selected in a random manner, an attempt to run a statistical test would be pointless. If this *were* a random sample, what hypotheses would be tested, and what test would be the most appropriate?

Exercise 2: Suppose we granted, on the basis of the data, that income had changed in a different way than education had changed. Has status congruence increased or decreased?

graph theory

The mathematical technique we now turn to is really just a complicated kind of set theory, but it has become important enough to deserve a name of its own. Graph theory deals not only with a set of elements but with sets of binary relations between the elements. This statement can be embodied in a formal definition.

Consider a set $P = \{p\}$ of elements, called points, and the set L of lines connecting these points pairwise. Then a graph G is the set P along with some subset of L.

The terminology "points" and "lines" suggests geometry, and indeed part of the fun of graph theory is drawing the figures. But the geometric interpretation is not the only one possible. The points can be elements of any kind, and the lines indicate binary relations of any type. ("Binary" simply means that we connect two points at a time.)

A familiar sociological interpretation is the sociogram. There are many different ways of constructing sociograms; one method is to observe a group of people and see who interacts with whom. We can represent the people by points and draw a line to indicate which pairs of people interact.

In the previous chapter we discussed experiments using communication networks. Graphs are a natural way of expressing such networks. It is common to represent a formal organization by a chart, with lines indicating lines of authority. Obviously this diagram is a graph.

Because graph theory emphasizes relations and, moreover, enables us to speak of configurations of relations, it seems a natural tool for sociological investigation. In *A Natural Science of Society,* Radcliffe-Brown speaks of a need for "relational mathematics" in social science. Graph theory is the kind of mathematics he must have meant.

A few simple definitions are necessary to enable us to talk about graphs. First, we note that since every line connects two points, it is quite natural to label lines according to these points. Thus a line connecting points 1 and 2 would be labeled L_{12}; a line connecting points i and j would be L_{ij}. Two points connected by a line are said to be adjacent. If we have a series of lines of the form L_{ab}, L_{bc}, L_{cd} . . . L_{mn}, then we say there is a path between points a and n. Of course, there may be more than one path between two points. If the graph is composed in such a way that between any two points there is a path, then we say that the graph is "connected." We will deal almost exclusively with connected graphs.

The following three graphs illustrate these definitions. In Figure 2.3, points 1 and 2 are adjacent; points 1 and 4 are not. In this figure

FIGURE 2.3

there are two paths between points 1 and 4. They are: L_{12}, L_{24} and L_{12}, L_{23}, L_{34}. Notice that the path L_{23}, L_{34}, L_{42} "doubles back" on itself. For obvious reasons such a path is called a cycle. Figure 2.4 can be thought of as an unconnected graph of 4 points. (It is unconnected because there is no path between points 1 and 3.) Notice, however, that there would be no loss of generality in the decision to talk about only connected graphs; Figure 2.4 would then be thought of as two connected graphs, each having two points. In Figure 2.5 all points are adjacent to each other; such a graph is called complete.

If we allow only one line (at most) to be drawn between two points and if we make no distinction between the line from point A to point B and the line from point B to point A (i.e., if the lines are not directed), then our graphs are called simple graphs. We can make a number of measurements on such graphs. One was introduced in an earlier chapter, when we talked about the "centrality" of a communication network. (Notice that centrality is defined only for connected graphs.)

FIGURE 2.4

There is another measurement we can make. We said that Figure 2.5 was "complete" because all points are adjacent to each other; Figures 2.3 and 2.4 are incomplete. We can get a numerical measure of completeness by comparing the number of lines actually in a graph with the largest possible number of lines—that is, with the number of lines in the set L. What is this largest possible number of lines?

FIGURE 2.5

Consider a graph of n points. Single out a particular point. How many lines radiate out from it? Because there are $(n-1)$ other points, there could be at most $(n-1)$ lines. If this statement is true for any point, it is true for all n of them; therefore, the number of lines radiating out is $n(n-1)$. But we agreed to make no distinction between a line from A to B and a line from B to A; thus any line radiating from A to B is also a line from B to A, and the largest possible number of lines is $1/2n(n-1)$.

Exercise: Try out the formula on a number of complete graphs.

We can now define an index. If there are m lines in a graph of n points, the degree of completeness is given by:

$$D = \frac{m}{\frac{1}{2}n(n-1)} = \frac{2m}{n(n-1)}$$

For a complete graph, $D = 1$; for a graph with no lines at all, $D = 0$.

Exercise 1: Compute D for Figures 2.3 and 2.4. Unlike centrality, completeness can be defined on incomplete graphs.

Exercise 2: What is the minimum number of lines in a connected graph of n points?

An interesting interpretation can be made of D. In the section on sets we used a formula for homogeneity,

$$H = \frac{\Sigma X^2}{(\Sigma X)^2}$$

which is equal to 1 for a completely homogeneous set. We can develop a somewhat better index based on graphs. We can draw a line between two points if and only if they represent members who have the same income. For a completely homogeneous group, this graph will be complete, and $D = 1$. For a completely heterogeneous group, there will be no lines, and $D = 0$.

Another way of stating this is that all people in the same category will be connected by lines. Any category, then, is a complete graph. But there can be no lines between people in different categories. Using this fact, we can give a formula for D (using X_i as before to indicate the number of people—or points—in category i) for a group of size n:

$$D = \frac{\Sigma X_i^2 - n}{n^2 - n}$$

(Note: this formula works only for transitive relations.)

Centrality and completeness are properties of simple graphs and have sociological interpretations. But we can get many more applications of graph theory by enriching graphs in various ways. First, though, we must develop an algebraic representation of graph theory.

matrices

So far we have been content just to draw our graphs, but for any abstract discussion, an algebraic language is useful. This is a convenient place to introduce matrices, because they have a very natural interpretation in graph theory. We will find matrix algebra useful later also, especially in the sections on Markov chains and games.

To the nonmathematician the very word "matrix" has a rather mysterious ring. He may have heard that A times B isn't always equal to B times A, or that the product of two matrices may be 0 without either of the factors being 0, all of which sounds very obscure. Actually a matrix is a very simple thing; it is nothing but a rectangular array of symbols. (Usually these symbols are numbers, but any symbols for which some algebraic laws have been defined may be used.) The symbols, called entries, are arranged in rows and columns. If there are m rows and n columns we call it an $m \times n$ matrix. If there are as many rows as columns, we call it a square matrix. Graphs will be represented by square matrices, but we will by no means be confined to them later.

This description does not exclude the possibility that a matrix might have only one row, or only one column, or indeed only one row and only one column. A matrix with only one row is called a row vector; a matrix with only one column is a column vector. For some purposes, a matrix can be thought of as a combination of vectors. Let us take a simple example.

Suppose we have an army unit of 5 captains, 10 sergeants, and 20 privates. One way to describe this unit would be to write the numbers in a row: (5, 10, 20). Of course, anyone reading this description would have to know the meaning of a position, but as soon as this meaning was established there would be no problem. Another unit with 7 captains, no sergeants, and 25 privates would be described by (7, 0, 25); a third unit might be (5, 5, 5). Each of these sets of numbers is a row vector. We could just as well have written them as columns. If all three units together compromise some new grouping, A, we can represent it by the following array:

$$A = \begin{matrix} 5 & 10 & 20 \\ 7 & 0 & 25 \\ 5 & 5 & 5 \end{matrix}$$

This is a square matrix. If we wished to represent such a grouping abstractly, we could write it thus:

$$A = \begin{matrix} a_{11} & a_{12} & a_{13} \\ a_{21} & a_{22} & a_{23} \\ a_{31} & a_{32} & a_{33} \end{matrix}$$

The little numbers (called subscripts) have no numerical significance; they only indicate position. (We could just as well have used letters.) The first subscript tells you which unit we are talking about; the second tells you whether the symbol represents captains, sergeants, or privates. Order, of course, is vitally important. A unit described by $(5, 10, 15)$ is quite different from one described by $(15, 10, 5)$.

matrix algebra

Two matrices, say, X and Y, are equal if and only if their corresponding entries are equal. Using the example above, we would say that two army groups were "equal" only if they had the same number of captains, the same number of sergeants, and the same number of privates. It follows that two matrices cannot be equal if they do not have the same number of rows and the same number of columns.

To add matrices together we add corresponding entries. Thus if two army units, $A = (1, 2, 3)$ and $B = (3, 4, 5)$, are combined into one, the new one will be $A + B = C = (4, 6, 8)$. This result is obvious; if we had 1 captain in the first group and 3 in the second, we would end up with 4 captains—unless someone were demoted. Subtraction is defined in an exactly analogous manner: subtract corresponding entries.

We might expect to find multiplication defined in the same way: multiply corresponding entries. For some specialized purposes this is done, as we will see later in the method for identifying cliques. Usually, however, matrix multiplication is done by rows and columns. If we have two matrices, A and B, such that A has as many columns as B has rows, then their product, $C = AB$, is formed by entries created by multiplying each element in a row of A with the corresponding element in a column of B. The general formula for each element is:

$$c_{ik} = \Sigma a_{ij}b_{jk}$$

For a two-by-two matrix the formula is:

$$AB = \begin{pmatrix} a_{11} & a_{12} \\ a_{21} & a_{22} \end{pmatrix}\begin{pmatrix} b_{11} & b_{12} \\ b_{21} & b_{22} \end{pmatrix}$$

$$= \begin{pmatrix} a_{11}b_{11} + a_{12}b_{21} & a_{11}b_{12} + a_{12}b_{22} \\ a_{21}b_{11} + a_{22}b_{21} & a_{21}b_{12} + a_{22}b_{22} \end{pmatrix}$$

A numerical example may be helpful:

$$\begin{pmatrix} 1 & 2 \\ 2 & 3 \end{pmatrix}\begin{pmatrix} 2 & 1 \\ 1 & 2 \end{pmatrix} = \begin{pmatrix} 2+2 & 1+4 \\ 4+3 & 2+6 \end{pmatrix} = \begin{pmatrix} 4 & 5 \\ 7 & 8 \end{pmatrix}$$

Notice that two matrices need not be the same "shape" to be multiplied. Suppose, for example, that we had a matrix $D = (d_{11},d_{12})$ and the matrix A as above. The product DA can be formed:

$$DA = (d_{11}, d_{12}) \begin{pmatrix} a_{11} & a_{12} \\ a_{21} & a_{22} \end{pmatrix} = (d_{11}a_{11} + d_{12}a_{21},\ d_{11}a_{12} + d_{12}a_{22})$$

But the product AD cannot be formed. (Why?)

This series of definitions seems useful, but the independent-minded reader will want to ask why such strange definitions were adopted at all. He also may ask if this operation has any uses for the sociologist. Perhaps an example will answer both questions.

Suppose that in some city there are 1,000 Negroes. This year 600 of them live in segregated areas, which we will call S areas, and 400 live in "non-S" areas. From previous experience we know that every year, 4/5 of those living in S areas remain there; 1/5 move to non-S areas. Furthermore, 1/2 of those living in non-S areas stay there; 1/2 move to S areas.

If the same pattern continues, how many Negroes will be living in

S areas next year? (Of course we are assuming no changes in the total Negro population from birth, death, migration, etc.) First, we can represent the distribution of Negroes by a row vector **(600, 400)**. The changes can be represented by what is called a transition matrix:

$$\begin{pmatrix} \frac{4}{5} & \frac{1}{5} \\ \frac{1}{2} & \frac{1}{2} \end{pmatrix}$$

The distribution vector for next year is given by:

$$(600,\ 400) \begin{pmatrix} \frac{4}{5} & \frac{1}{5} \\ \frac{1}{2} & \frac{1}{2} \end{pmatrix} = (480 + 200,\ 120 + 200) = (680,\ 320)$$

We expect that there will be 680 Negroes living in S areas next year. These areas will be made up of 4/5 of those living there now, plus 1/2 of those now living in non-S areas. We will see in the next chapter that this matrix can be used to do several interesting things, but we have carried this example far enough to show why the "queer" law of multiplication is used. Let us now return to graph theory.

Graphs and Matrices

There are many ways in which we can represent graphs by matrices. In the previous chapter we represented an organization chart (which is a kind of graph) by a matrix in which entries represent distance from the top. We could have used matrices to represent communication networks; an entry in the matrix would be distance between two points. These are special matrices, constructed for special purposes.

A more fundamental kind of matrix can be constructed to show the underlying pattern of relationships. We will call it the structure matrix. (Actually, there is more than one way to construct a structure matrix. We will consider only "vertex-vertex" matrices.) The entries in this matrix consist of 0's and 1's, and it is constructed by following this simple rule: If point i is adjacent to point j, then entry ij is 1; otherwise it is 0. Some graphs and their matrix representations are shown in Figures 2.6(A) through (E). As an exercise the reader might check the correspondences. (Rows and columns are numbered consecutively.)

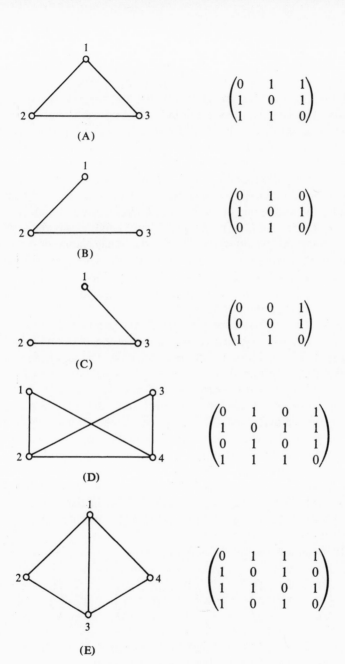

FIGURE 2.6

Figure 2.6(A) is a complete graph; all points are adjacent to each other. Therefore, all entries in the matrix are 1, except entries 11, 22, and 33. These entries are said to lie on the "main diagonal" of the matrix. The fact that they are 0 indicates that we do not consider a point to be adjacent to itself. (Of course, we can adopt a convention that it is, if we want to. Then every entry in the matrix corresponding to a complete graph would be 1.)

Look at Figures 2.6(B) and (C). If we rotated them around on the page we could superimpose one on the other. They are identical except for the numbering of the points. Similiarly, if we "unfolded" Figure 2.6(D), we could fit it on top of Figure 2.6(E); only the numbering of the points would differ. Clearly, the nomenclature of the points is arbitrary. Figures 2.6(B) and (C) have the same *structure,* as do Figures 2.6(D) and (E). But superimposing one graph on the other is a rather haphazard way of determining anything; let us see if we can do it by operating on their matrices.

Look at the matrices for Figures 2.6(B) and (C). Figure 2.6(B) has two rows with one entry of 1 and two entries of 0, and it has one row with two entries of 1 and one entry of 0. The matrix for Figure 2.6(C) can be described in the same way. The only difference between the two matrices is the arrangement of rows and columns. Is there a way in which we can algebraically switch rows and columns around so that Figures 2.6(B) and (C) will be the same? (Remember that we are subject to the restriction that entries on the main diagonal must be 0.) Indeed there is; we can multiply the matrix for Figure 2.6(B) by "permutation matrices."

A permutation matrix is a square matrix, every row of which contains exactly one entry of 1; all other entries in that row are 0. In every column there is exactly one entry of 1; all other entries in that column are 0.

Here are a few permutation matrices:

$$Q = \begin{pmatrix} 0 & 0 & 1 \\ 1 & 0 & 0 \\ 0 & 1 & 0 \end{pmatrix} \quad R = \begin{pmatrix} 0 & 1 & 0 \\ 0 & 0 & 1 \\ 1 & 0 & 0 \end{pmatrix} \quad T = \begin{pmatrix} 0 & 0 & 1 \\ 0 & 1 & 0 \\ 1 & 0 & 0 \end{pmatrix}$$

There is an interesting relation between Q and R. If we write the rows of R as columns and the columns of R as rows, then the resulting matrix is identical with Q. For this reason, R is called the transpose of

Q and can be written $R = Q^{-1}$. We shall use this transpose relation in a moment.

Exercise: What is the transpose of T?

If we have a structure matrix, S, and we multiply it by a permutation matrix, P, to get PS, the rows will be switched. Multiplication of S by the transpose of P, to get SP^{-1}, would have the effect of switching columns. (Note that we multiplied on the *left* by P, on the *right* by P^{-1}.) Neither switching columns alone nor switching rows alone would be sufficient, because either procedure might put an entry of 1 on the main diagonal of the structure matrix, which is "against the rules." But if we form the product PSP^{-1}, we will have a structure matrix that differs from S only in that the rows and columns have been switched around. This new matrix would then correspond to a graph that is structurally identical to the graph represented by S. It would differ only in the numbering of points.

An example can be given based on Figures 2.6(B) and (C). (An example, of course, does not prove the statement. To prove it is not difficult but would require somewhat more development of matrix algebra than we have room for here. The interested reader can consult any standard text on matrix theory or modern algebra.)

The structure matrix for Figure 2.6(B) is:

$$B = \begin{pmatrix} 0 & 1 & 0 \\ 1 & 0 & 1 \\ 0 & 1 & 0 \end{pmatrix}$$

For P and P^{-1} we use the following:

$$P = \begin{pmatrix} 1 & 0 & 0 \\ 0 & 0 & 1 \\ 0 & 1 & 0 \end{pmatrix} = P^{-1}$$

The reader may verify the following matrix multiplications:

$$PB = \begin{pmatrix} 1 & 0 & 0 \\ 0 & 0 & 1 \\ 0 & 1 & 0 \end{pmatrix}\begin{pmatrix} 0 & 1 & 0 \\ 1 & 0 & 1 \\ 0 & 1 & 0 \end{pmatrix} = \begin{pmatrix} 0 & 1 & 0 \\ 0 & 1 & 0 \\ 1 & 0 & 1 \end{pmatrix}$$

and

$$PBP^{-1} = \begin{pmatrix} 0 & 1 & 0 \\ 0 & 1 & 0 \\ 1 & 0 & 1 \end{pmatrix} \begin{pmatrix} 1 & 0 & 0 \\ 0 & 0 & 1 \\ 0 & 1 & 0 \end{pmatrix} = \begin{pmatrix} 0 & 0 & 1 \\ 0 & 0 & 1 \\ 1 & 1 & 0 \end{pmatrix}$$

This last matrix corresponds to Figure 2.6(C). We can make the following generalization: Two graphs are isomorphic if and only if their matrices X and Y are related by an equation $PXP^{-1} = Y$ for some permutation matrix P.

Exercise 1: Why are you sure that there is no permutation matrix that can make the matrix for A identical to the matrix for B?

Exercise 2: Using a 4×4 permutation matrix, show that D and E are isomorphic.

This method has so far had rather limited application in sociology. We could use it to show rigorously that two groups (or the same group under different conditions) did or did not have the same structure. For example, groups trying to solve the same kind of problem might tend to take on the same structure. I know of no attempts to study this phenomenon.

But I would like to speculate that there may be some more important uses for this method eventually. We have defined what we mean when we say that two relational structures are the same. Specifications might be given to determine whether two social structures are the same. (In many cases, social structures may have several different kinds of relations between elements. Present graph theory cannot handle this kind of structure.)

If this were done, we could test some interesting hypotheses. For example, we sometimes hear it said that the United States and the Soviet Union have the same basic social structure. In what sense is this true? More generally, much of "functional" theory deals with similarity of structures; graph theory can give us a rigorous language with which to discuss this similarity.

Cliques
Let us turn from this speculation to a more prosaic use of the structure matrix—the interpretation of graphs as sociograms. Points

represent people, and a line between two points indicates that the two people are friends. We will now define a "clique" as three or more people who are mutual friends. For example, in Figure 2.7, 2, 3, and 4 form a clique; 1 is not a member of a clique. (He is a friend of 2 but they do not share a mutual friend.)

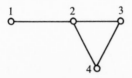

FIGURE 2.7

Here, it is easy enough to pick out a clique visually, because the clique forms a complete subgraph (i.e., it is a complete graph that is part of another graph.) But with a very large sociogram (say of 100 people or more), it is not easy to draw the lines, much less pick out cliques. So an algebraic method of picking out cliques was developed,[8] which we will now consider.

We would like to get a matrix M with entries m_{ik}, which are greater than 0 if and only if person i and person k are friends and i and k share a mutual friend, person j. We start with the structure matrix S. If this is squared (by matrix multiplication) we have, by definition, a matrix S^2, which has elements like this:

$$S^2 = \Sigma_j s_{ij} s_{jk}$$

Such an entry will always be 0 unless i and k have a mutual friend; that is, $s_{ij} = 1$ and $s_{jk} = 1$. However, S^2 does not contain enough information; one possibility is that i and k have a common friend but are not themselves friends. So we multiply S^2 by S (by *element-wise* multiplication). The resulting matrix is M, and has elements defined as follows:

$$m_{ik} = (\Sigma s_{ij} s_{jk})\, s_{ik}$$

This will be 0 if and only if at least one of the factors is 0. If this entry is not 0, it shows that i, j, and k are mutual friends; that is, they form a clique. Let us illustrate with the 4-person group used above.

The structure matrix is:

$$S = \begin{pmatrix} 0 & 1 & 0 & 0 \\ 1 & 0 & 1 & 1 \\ 0 & 1 & 0 & 1 \\ 0 & 1 & 1 & 0 \end{pmatrix}$$

By matrix multiplication we get S^2, which the reader may verify as:

$$S^2 = \begin{pmatrix} 1 & 0 & 1 & 1 \\ 0 & 3 & 1 & 1 \\ 1 & 1 & 2 & 1 \\ 1 & 1 & 1 & 2 \end{pmatrix}$$

Multiplying this matrix element-by-element with S gives us

$$S^2 \times S = \begin{pmatrix} 0 & 0 & 0 & 0 \\ 0 & 0 & 1 & 1 \\ 0 & 1 & 0 & 1 \\ 0 & 1 & 1 & 0 \end{pmatrix} = M$$

From this matrix we can see that 1 is not in any clique, because all entries in his row and column are 0. Numbers 2, 3, and 4 are members of a clique, as can be seen by the fact that entries 23, 34, 42, and their transpose entries are not 0.

Exercise: Figure 2.8 is a graph representing a group with two cliques, having one member in common.

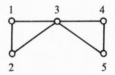

FIGURE 2.8

Use the matrix method to identify the cliques. Does the matrix M give you a way of identifying the common member?

A method for identifying cliques hardly needs much justification.

Sociologists are aware of the importance of personal influence on such things as voting behavior; cliques are powerful concentrations of influence. We could easily multiply examples.

Further applications are possible if we leave the sociogram interpretation. If the elements are "cultural items," then a clique would be a "cultural complex" and the matrix method would amount to a kind of factor analysis.

In conclusion, we might say that the structure matrix summarizes basic information about whatever set we are studying. Some people have remarked that the sociogram is the most sociological of all research tools because it lays bare group structure. The same could be said of graphs, which, in a way, are generalizations of sociograms. In the next section we enrich graph theory by giving the relations more properties; then we will be dealing with "valuated" structure matrices.

directed graphs

So far we have not made a distinction between a line from point *A* to point *B* and a line from point *B* to point *A*. If we distinguish these, we are dealing with directed graphs or digraphs. Such graphs can give us a much more realistic picture of social relationships. We are quite aware that many social relationships are "directed" in this sense. If John loves Mary, the conclusion by no means follows that Mary loves John. If Frank admires Harry, there is no guarantee that Harry reciprocates. And if Henry is my boss, I am not his. So giving direction to our lines gives us an increase in realism. But there is an accompanying increase in mathematical complexity. First, we have to note that we must allow two lines between any two points—one in each direction. To go thoroughly into digraph theory we would have to redefine many basic terms, such as connectedness, completeness, path, cycle, and so on. So we will not go very deeply into diagraph theory here, but will just touch on a few topics. Fortunately for the reader, there is a very thorough book devoted entirely to the subject.[9]

Trees

One of the simplest uses of directed graphs is the representation of hierarchies. Here we permit only one line between any two points, and a line from point i to point j indicates that person i is higher in the hierarchy than person j. We have already used this kind of device in the form of an organization chart. Let us try to use a form of the structure matrix to represent such a graph. (This will be different from the matrix used to measure status in the previous chapter. The reader should not feel discomfited when he finds that there is more than one way to represent concepts mathematically. We choose our algebra to fit our purposes; our purpose in this section is better served by a bare structure matrix.) The principle used in constructing the matrix is quite simple: If there is a line from point i to point j, then entry ij is 1; otherwise it is 0. Because we permit only one line, if entry ij is 1, then entry ji is 0. To take the simplest example, if Albert is Bennet's boss, the diagraph is $A \longrightarrow B$ and the matrix is

$$\begin{pmatrix} 0 & 1 \\ 0 & 0 \end{pmatrix}$$

where the first row is Albert's and the second is Bennet's.

A basic principle of hierarchical organizations is that no one should have more than one direct superior. In terms of the structure matrix, this principle means that no column should contain more than one nonzero entry. In terms of diagraphs it means that there should be no cycles. A graph with no cycles is called a tree. The requirement that an organization be depictable as a tree is, of course, normative, not descriptive, as any observer of organizations knows.

Trees can be used to represent other things besides hierarchies. For example, any branching process can be represented by a tree. Suppose we are studying some city, which we have divided up into areas (natural areas, census tracts, etc.), and we classify each area as being more than 50 percent white (a), more than 50 percent Negro (b), or half white, half Negro (c). We wish to trace the "career" of some single area over a series of years. We will use points to indicate successive observations. If we start with a predominantly white area, at the time of the next observation it may have remained the same, or become predominantly Negro, or become mixed (see Figure 2.9).

For each one of these possible outcomes there are, in the next observation period, three more possible outcomes. We could draw a continually branching tree to depict these outcomes. No attempt will be made to draw it here, because it quickly becomes very clumsy. This tree, of course, only indicates the logical possibilities. But the sociologist can utilize a tree like this one by going out and observing the frequency with which transitions from *a* to *b* or *a* to *c*, or *b* to *c* or *c* to *a*, and so on occur. Having that information, he can calculate the proba-

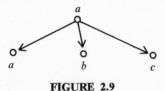

FIGURE 2.9

bility that after a certain number of years, some given area will be predominantly white, predominantly Negro, or exactly balanced. We will perform this kind of calculation in the next chapter.

Sociograms

We have already mentioned the use of graphs as sociograms. If we construct the sociogram by asking members of the population whom they like best, the most natural representation is a diagraph (because if *A* likes *B*, it does not follow that *B* likes *A*). In this diagraph we permit 0, 1, or 2 lines between two points. We can illustrate with an imaginary group of four girls. Each is asked which two of the other girls she likes best. The results are:

> Abigail likes Clarise and Denise
> Beulah likes Abigail and Denise
> Clarise likes Abigail and Denise
> Denise likes Abigail and Clarise

The resulting digraph is shown in Figure 2.10.

FIGURE 2.10

The structure matrix, constructed as in the last section, is:

$$
\begin{array}{c}
 & \begin{array}{cccc} A & B & C & D \end{array} \\
\begin{array}{c} A \\ B \\ C \\ D \end{array} &
\begin{pmatrix}
0 & 0 & 1 & 1 \\
1 & 0 & 0 & 1 \\
1 & 0 & 0 & 1 \\
1 & 0 & 1 & 0
\end{pmatrix}
\end{array}
$$

The sum in each column is the popularity rating of the girl. Obviously Abigail is a "star" and Beulah is an "isolate."

Does this matrix (sometimes called a sociomatrix) have any advantage over the sociogram? After all, it contains no more information. In a fairly large group it has obvious visual advantages; it is easier to sum up entries in a column than to count the number of lines converging on a point. In addition, we can perform certain operations with the matrix. For example, we can find the number of mutual choices by a very simple operation. (A mutual choice is when A chooses B and B chooses A.) We simply take the transpose of the sociomatrix and perform element-by-element multiplication. Then the number of mutual choices is half the number of nonzero entries in the resulting matrix.

Taking our preceding matrix as an example:

$$
\begin{pmatrix}
0 & 0 & 1 & 1 \\
1 & 0 & 0 & 1 \\
1 & 0 & 0 & 1 \\
1 & 0 & 1 & 0
\end{pmatrix}
$$

Its transpose is:

$$
\begin{pmatrix}
0 & 1 & 1 & 1 \\
0 & 0 & 0 & 0 \\
1 & 0 & 0 & 1 \\
1 & 1 & 1 & 0
\end{pmatrix}
$$

The reader may confirm that the element-wise product is:

$$
\begin{pmatrix}
0 & 0 & 1 & 1 \\
0 & 0 & 0 & 0 \\
1 & 0 & 0 & 1 \\
1 & 0 & 1 & 0
\end{pmatrix}
$$

There are six nonzero entries; thus there are three mutual choices.

Exercise: What is the sociological importance of the number of mutual choices in a group?

After this all-too-brief look at digraphs, we turn our attention to a different way of enriching graph theory.

signed graphs

From here on we will ignore the direction of lines and permit at most one line between two points. But we will now distinguish "positive" and "negative" lines. Many relations of interest to the sociologist have this property. People not only like each other; some dislike each other. For example, some countries are allies; others are enemies. Some things are similar to each other; others are dissimilar.

This phenomenon can be easily represented with graphs. To indicate that two people like each other, we attach a +1 to the line connecting them. To indicate that two people dislike each other, we attach a −1 to the line. In Figure 2.11, *A* and *B* like each other but dislike, and are disliked by, *C:*

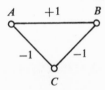

FIGURE 2.11

Such a graph is called a signed graph or simply a "sigraph." (The thought may occur to the reader that there is no reason for not attaching such signs to the lines of a digraph. Indeed, there is not. However, such a procedure gets too complicated to be shown here. But if the reader is so inclined, he may develop the theory of sidigraphs for himself.)

Sigraphs are particularly interesting when they contain cycles. (The reader will recall that a cycle is a path that starts and ends at the same point without crossing itself.) If we put a $+1$ or -1 on each of the component lines of a cycle and then multiply these numbers together, we get either $+1$ or -1 as the product. If it is $+1$, we say the cycle is positive; if it is -1, we say the cycle is negative.

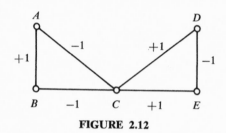

FIGURE 2.12

Figure 2.12 is a sigraph in which there are two cycles. Cycle *ABC* is positive; cycle *CDE* is negative. Care should be exercised in counting cycles. In Figure 2.13 there are three cycles: *ABC, CBD,* and *ABDC.*

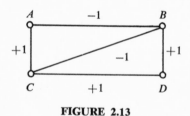

FIGURE 2.13

Exercise: Determine if each of the cycles is positive or negative.

There is a sociological interpretation of these cycles. A common observation is that if two people are friends, then if a third person is a friend of one, he will usually be a friend of the other. We say "usually" because this statement is by no means invariably true. If Albert has a friend Bill and a friend Charlie, Bill and Charlie might not even know each other, or they might be enemies. (Two men who love the same woman may not love each other.) But usually, Bill and Charlie will be friends. Such a situation is stable, whereas the situation in which they are enemies is unstable and will tend to change. (We will not investigate the case where they do not know each other.)

A further common observation is that if two people are friends, the enemies of one will usually be enemies of the other. If Albert and Bill are friends and Desmond is an enemy of Albert, then usually Bill will be an enemy of Desmond. Again, we say *usually*. The statement is not always true. (Find a counterexample in international politics.) The usual case we will call stable; the case where a person's friend is a friend of his enemy we will call unstable, because this situation will tend to change.

If we use graphs to represent stable situations, using +1 to indicate friendship and −1 to indicate enmity, then each cycle is positive (see Figure 2.14).

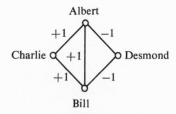

FIGURE 2.14

In the graph of an unstable situation, there will be negative cycles.

Exercise: Draw the sigraph of an unstable situation. Note that not all cycles need be negative.

Let us formalize the above. First, we make the following mathematical definition: A sigraph, all of whose cycles are positive, is called balanced. If there is at least one negative cycle, the sigraph is unbalanced.

Next we make a sociological assumption: A situation that is represented by a balanced graph is stable. A situation that is represented by an unbalanced graph is unstable and will tend to change in the direction of balance. (Note that these are assumptions about the real social world. We do not claim that they in any way "follow" from the mathematics.)

Let us make one further assumption, then proceed to an illustration. We assume that an unstable situation will tend to change to a

51

stable one in the simplest possible way. By "simplest" we mean the way that requires the fewest changes.

Let us suppose that there are three countries: Xenia, Yenzu, and Zaliland—for simplicity we will call them X, Y, and Z respectively. Assume that Y and Z are implacable enemies whose relationship will not change. Suppose that X finds itself in the position of being allied to both countries. This situation is unstable, and one of two things must happen: either X becomes an enemy of Y or X becomes an enemy of Z. From our point of view each result is equally likely, for each involves one change and leads to a stable situation.

Suppose now that we have further information indicating that Xenia is allied to Woesia, which in turn is allied to Yenzu. This situation is unstable and is represented by a sigraph (Figure 2.15).

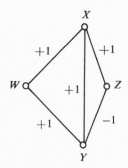

FIGURE 2.15

But our prediction regarding change must be altered. Nothing would be solved if X became an enemy of Y, for then cycle WXY would be negative, and at least one more change would be required to bring balance. But if X instead became an enemy of Z, everything would be settled; all cycles would be positive and the graph would be balanced. So we predict that X is more likely to become an enemy of Z than of Y.

Harary has produced an interesting structure theorem that can be stated as follows: A complete graph can be balanced if and only if (1) all relations are positive, or (2) there are exactly two coalitions such that all members of the same coalition are joined by positive lines and members of different coalitions are joined by negative lines.[10]

Three or more coalitions are inherently unstable. One interpretation of this theorem is that one-party and two-party political systems are stable but that multiparty systems are not.

Exercise: Try proving this theorem by first constructing a graph with two coalitions and then trying to add a third coalition in such a way that the graph remains balanced. Remember then when you add the third, it must be joined by negative lines to both the previous coalitions.

conclusion: sets and graphs

Set theory, and its special branch, graph theory, are mathematical systems in their own right and as such, are of interest to mathematicians. But they are also languages that can be useful to the sociologist who is attempting to record and define social reality. Populations of people, of cities, or of attitudes can be thought of as sets; any classification of elements can be thought of as decomposition into subsets. Comparisons between populations can be characterized in the language of functions (mappings, transformations, etc.). Relations can be represented by graphs; structures of relations can be analyzed by matrix algebra. Because the main business of sociologists is the description and analysis of relational structures of a particular sort, such a language should be of more than passing interest.

Exercises—Chapter II

1. All sociologists are familiar to some extent with sampling theory. Such theory can be expressed in set language (e.g., a representative sample is a subset having the same structure as the population). Is there any advantage to thinking of sampling in these terms?

2. "Function" as used by the sociologist and "function" as used by the mathematician should probably be thought of as two different words. However, some forms of sociological-anthropological functionalism strongly suggest the idea of a mathematical function. Suppose a social scientist believes that whenever certain characteristics are present in a culture, then certain other characteristics will be pres-

ent also. (This is *one* version of functionalism.) If we call the first characteristics set X and the second set Y, then "occurring together" (or "implying the other") is a function (or if you prefer, a "correspondence") in the mathematical sense. Do other forms of sociological functionalism use the idea of a mathematical function in some way?

3. When one "classifies" the elements of some set, we say formally that the set is divided into equivalence classes. An equivalence class is a subset in which all the members are related by an equivalence relation. An equivalence relation is a binary relation that is reflexive, symmetric, and transitive. If we write aRb to show that there is a relation between elements a and b, then if aRa, the relation is reflexive; if aRb implies bRa, the relation is symmetric; if aRb and bRc imply aRc, then the relation is transitive.

For example, if R means "is in the same income bracket as," then clearly, John is in the same income bracket as himself; if he is in the same bracket as Joe, then Joe is in the same bracket as John; and if Joe is in the same bracket as Tom, John, and Tom are in the same bracket. If we use points to represent the members of the set and draw a line between two points if they are in the same equivalence class, then the graph depicting the equivalence class is complete. (Why?)

Most relations of interest to sociologists are *not* equivalence relations; they violate one or more of the characteristics listed. For example, if John interacts with Joe and Joe with Tom, the conclusion does not follow that John interacts with Tom. (Thus "interacts with" is not transitive.) The text has shown that completeness is a good measure of homogeneity for equivalence relations. What is the interpretation of completeness for nonequivalence relations?

4. Harary's structure theorem seems to be a plausible explanation for some political facts (e.g., dictatorships and two-party systems do seem more stable than multiparty systems such as existed in France in the post-World War II era). But if we look at, say, the United States, we may question how realistic it is to call it a two-party system, because both major parties are deeply divided on some issues. Yet the system seems stable. How can we reconcile this observation with Harary's theorem?

5. Does the literature on groups support the assumption that stability and instability correspond to balanced and unbalanced graphs? (You might, for instance, look at Homans' *The Human Group*.)

NOTES

1. Herbert Simon, *Models of Man* (New York: Wiley, 1957), chap. 5.

2. George Homans, *Social Behavior: Its Elementary Forms* (New York: Harcourt, Brace & World, 1961), p. 11.

3. John Kemeny, *Random Essays on Mathematics, Education and Computers* (Englewood Cliffs, N.J.: Prentice-Hall, 1964).

4. T. B. Bottomore, *Sociology: A Guide to Problems and Literature* (Englewood Cliffs, N.J.: Prentice-Hall, 1962), pp. 109 ff.

5. Mary Hesse, *Forces and Fields* (Camden, N.J.: Thomas Nelson, 1962).

6. G. Lenski, "Status Crystallization: A Non-vertical Dimension of Status," in *American Sociological Review,* 19 (August 1964), 403–413.

7. James Geschwender, "Social Structure and the Negro Revolt: An Examination of Some Hypotheses," in *Social Forces,* 43 (December 1964), 248–256.

8. Frank Harary and I. Ross, "A Procedure for Clique Detection Using the Group Matrix," in *Sociometry,* 20 (September 1957), 205–215.

9. Frank Harary, Robert Norman, and Dorwin Cartwright, *Structural Models* (New York: Wiley, 1965).

10. *Ibid.,* p. 342.

markov chains and game theory

Lewis Carroll's Alice was looking with great curiosity at the odd collection of things the White Knight had in his saddle. When she came across a mousetrap she could not resist asking why he had that, since it was unlikely that there would be mice on the back of his horse. "It may be unlikely," he replied, "but if there were any I wouldn't care to have them running about!" We all must deal with possibilities, with things that may or may not happen, and we must prepare, to some extent, for different contingencies. In this chapter we look at the mathematical theory that enables us to deal with uncertainties, and discuss the uses of this theory in sociology.

probability

In this chapter we will look at some theories that are rather different from those preceding in that they are based on concepts of probability. We will begin by examining "Markov chains," which are especially useful in the study of social change. Then we will look at game theory, which forces us to reconsider the notion of rational behavior. Probability enters in the form of stochastic process and expected outcome.

"Stochastic" derives from the Greek word meaning "to guess." Frequently we cannot say exactly how a certain process will go, but we can make an educated guess about it. In a pinball machine, for example, the ball may follow a very complicated path after it has been released; no one can predict how many bounces, in what directions, the ball will take. But an experienced player can guess about how many points he will score after the ball has hit two or three bumpers. We may contrast this process with a "deterministic" process, in which we know fairly precisely what will happen. For example, when a clock has been wound we can say with great accuracy where the hands will be after a certain length of time (given initial position of the hands).

"Expected outcome" is a similar concept. If we toss a fair coin $2n$ times, we expect heads about n times. We cannot predict the outcome of any particular toss, and we know that in some sequence we may get all heads or all tails. But in the long run we expect to get n heads. We may contrast this result with a deterministic outcome. If we put a quarter in a candy dispenser for a 10-cent bar, we expect to get 15 cents change—every time. We would not be happy if we sometimes got 12 cents and sometimes 18 cents, even though our losses and gains might eventually even out.

There are conflicting views on the applicability of the concept of probability in describing the real world. Some hold that a fundamental uncertainty is present in all predictions, especially predictions about human behavior. Uncertainty results not just because we commit errors that could be reduced or even eliminated. Rather, indeterminacy is a fact of life that we have to accept at some level of analysis. Others feel that uncertainty is just an expression of ignorance; if we knew enough about the determinants of behavior, we could predict with perfect certainty. To return to the analogy of the pinball machine and the clock, we know that both are determined by the same laws of physics. With sufficient information about the tension of the springs, the composition of the ball and so on, we could predict the path of the ball quite accurately. Similarly, human behavior is just as determinate; we simply do not yet know enough about the basic principles.

I incline to the latter view. Whenever we use probability, it is as a calculating device. Underlying any process is a basically "knowable" mechanism, a "latent process" if you like. Because we cannot wait until this process is made manifest, we do what we can with our inadequate knowledge. At this stage in the development of sociology, it really doesn't make much of a difference which philosophical position you take. The mathematical techniques presented in this chapter will work for determinist and indeterminist alike.

markov chains

In the last chapter I introduced the idea of a distribution vector. To make our discussion more definite, suppose we have a city with 30 census tracts. For each tract we know the percent of the population that is Negro. We shall say that a tract can be in one of three states:

It can be all white (state 1)
It can be part white, part Negro (state 2)
It can be all Negro (state 3)

Translated into percentages, reasonable specifications could be:

State 1—less than 20 percent Negro
State 2—20–80 percent Negro
State 3—more than 80 percent Negro

At some time there is a definite distribution of tracts into states. Say that at time t_1 there are 10 tracts in state 1, 10 tracts in state 2, and 10 tracts in state 3. We will write n_{11} for the number of tracts in state 1 at time t_1; n_{12} for the number of tracts in state 2 at that time, and n_{13} for the number of tracts then in state 3. In our example we said $n_{11} = n_{12} = n_{13} = 10$. We can write this as a vector: $d_1 = $ **(10, 10, 10)**. At a later time, t_2, the distribution may have changed and we would represent it as $d_2 = (n_{21}, n_{22}, n_{23})$. This vector might be, say, **(5, 15, 10)**. The number of all-white tracts has decreased, the number of mixed tracts increased, and number of all-Negro tracts stayed the same. Later on we would find different distributions again: $d_3, d_4, \ldots . d_n$.

If these distributions are different from one another, some social process must be occurring, transforming the demographic structure. Let us represent this process by T. Then we can write:

$$d_1 T = d_2 \tag{1}$$

This equation represents what happens between times t_1 and t_2. If the same process continues from t_2 to t_3, we can write:

$$d_2 T = d_3 \tag{2}$$

We can substitute (1) into (2) to get

$$d_1 TT = d_3$$

or more simply

$$d_1 T^2 = d_3 \tag{2a}$$

If the process goes on as before from t_3 to t_4, then

$$d_3 T = d_4 \tag{3}$$

Substituting (2a) into (3) we get

$$(d_1 T^2)T = d_1 T^3 = d_4 \tag{3a}$$

It should be clear that the general formula is:

$$d_1 T^n = d_{n+1}$$

This means that if we know the initial distribution d_1 and the transformation T, we can predict the distribution after any number of time periods without having to calculate the intermediate distributions. (Predict, that is, with the assumption that the social process does not change.) A process described in this manner is called a Markov process, after the Russian mathematician A. A. Markov.

Obviously, a way of evaluating T would be very useful. We could use such a method to predict future demographic distributions or to investigate how the present distribution came into being. The letter T represents a transformation involving some social process. In our example, the process is the movement of people into and out of certain geographical areas. To fully understand T we would have to know what makes some Negroes move into areas inhabited by other Negroes, what makes some Negroes move into predominantly white areas, what makes some whites move out of areas that Negroes are moving into and so on. Detailed knowledge of these forces would give us the desired understanding of the demographic changes.

Unfortunately, we do not know the principles underlying such behavior, nor does it seem likely that we would have the necessary data to make predictions if we did know them. So we must do what we can with the information we have. Mainly, this information consists of records of past behavior.

If there were n_{11} tracts in state 1 at time t_1 and m of *these* tracts were in state 2 at time t_2, then $m/n_{11} = p_{12}$ is the proportion of tracts that have changed from state 1 to state 2. Similarly, we could find p_{13}, the proportion that moved from state 1 to state 3, and we could find p_{23}, the proportion of tracts that moved from state 2 to state 3. More generally:

$$p_{ij} = \frac{\text{number of tracts that were in state } i \text{ at time } t_1 \text{ that are in state } j \text{ at time } t_2}{\text{number of tracts in state } i \text{ at time } t_1}$$

Clearly, for any set of census tracts, for any given time period, we could construct 9 proportions like that above and could arrange them in a matrix, T, like this:

$$T = \begin{pmatrix} p_{11} & p_{12} & p_{13} \\ p_{21} & p_{22} & p_{23} \\ p_{31} & p_{32} & p_{33} \end{pmatrix}$$

This matrix allows us to calculate the effect of the transformation T. We make the assumption that p_{ij}, the proportion of tracts that moved from state i to state j, is also the *probability* that in the future a tract in state i will change to state j. Then T becomes a matrix of transition probabilities. Its repeated application to a distribution vector gives us a model of a stochastic process.

An Application to Sociology

There are a great many ways in which Markov chains can be used in sociology. They have been applied to such diverse subjects as labor mobility [1] and conformity experiments.[2] We will look in some detail at the construction of a processual index of segregation.[3] To understand this index we will need to examine different kinds of transition matrices and go a step or two further in matrix algebra.

Before moving on to sociology, let us make a simple mechanical model. Suppose we have a fairly deep cylindrical wastebasket, the bottom of which is divided into two equal areas, A and B, by a relatively low barrier. If we drop Ping-Pong balls into the basket, they are equally likely to fall into A or B. After they fall they will bounce; if the divider is low enough the balls will be equally likely to bounce up and down in the area into which they dropped or to bounce over into the other area. We can represent this process by a Markov chain.

Suppose we drop 12 balls in at random. (Whether they are dropped in one at a time or all together does not matter, so long as they don't interfere with each other.) Because area A equals area B, we may assume that 6 balls fall on one side of the barrier and 6 fall on the other. Then the initial distribution vector would be **(6, 6)**. If we wished, we could have made 7 balls fall on A; then the distribution vector would be **(7, 5)**. Or we could have dropped all the balls on B, so the vector would be **(0, 12)**. The transition matrix takes the rather uninteresting form:

$$T = \begin{pmatrix} p_{AA} & p_{AB} \\ p_{BA} & p_{BB} \end{pmatrix} = \begin{pmatrix} \frac{1}{2} & \frac{1}{2} \\ \frac{1}{2} & \frac{1}{2} \end{pmatrix}$$

In this matrix p_{AA} is the probability that a ball dropped on A will bounce up and fall back into A; p_{AB} is the probability that a ball dropped on A will bounce over into B and so on. How many balls do you expect to find in A after the first bounce? You can easily guess. But the number can be calculated by the formula $d_1 T = d_2$:

$$(6, 6) \begin{pmatrix} \frac{1}{2} & \frac{1}{2} \\ \frac{1}{2} & \frac{1}{2} \end{pmatrix} = (\tfrac{1}{2} \times 6 + \tfrac{1}{2} \times 6, \tfrac{1}{2} \times 6 + \tfrac{1}{2} \times 6) = (6, 6)$$

We expect to find 6 balls in A and 6 balls in B. The 6 in area A presumably are 3 of those that originally dropped in A plus 3 that bounced over from B.

Exercise: Suppose you moved the barrier so that A was twice as large as B. Set up the transition matrix. Assume that all the balls are dropped in B; how many balls do you expect in B after one bounce? After two bounces? (Hint: use $d_1 T^2 = d_3$.)

Notice how this process differs from a deterministic one. We made some assumptions about the probable course. After one bounce all the balls, or 3 or 9, or any other number up to 12, could possibly be in A. Six is the most likely number, but a different distribution would not make us lose faith in the laws of physics.

Absorbing States. We would expect that as long as the balls keep bouncing high enough, the distribution may keep changing. In one especially interesting kind of Markov chain, this is not the case. Let us return to our wastebasket and make a slight change: pour glue in the bottom on side B. Now when we drop balls in, those that land on side B will stay there; after the first bounce the balls that go from A to B will not be balanced by balls going from B to A. The transition matrix looks like this:

$$\begin{pmatrix} p_{AA} & p_{AB} \\ p_{BA} & p_{BB} \end{pmatrix} = \begin{pmatrix} \frac{1}{2} & \frac{1}{2} \\ 0 & 1 \end{pmatrix}$$

Side A is called a transient state and Side B is called an absorbing state. (For our example, "sticky state" might be better.) There is a theorem that states that if there is one absorbing state in a process, eventually all the elements end up in it. (There may be more than one absorbing state; the theorem states that all elements then end up in the set of absorbing states.)

There are many ways absorbing states can be used in sociology. Suppose we are conducting a study in which a rumor has been started in a group. We wish to determine how many people have heard it after a given time. Then at any moment, every member of the group is in one of two states: he has heard the rumor (state 1) or he has not (state 2). Clearly someone in state 2 can change to state 1, but no one in state 1 can change to state 2—so state 1 is an absorbing state.

For a different example, consider the process of unionization. (This was suggested to the author by a student in a seminar.) A company may at some time have no union (state 1), or it may have a company union (state 2), or it may have a regular union (state 3). Transitions between these states are possible, but decertification (transition *out* of state 3) is infrequent enough to be negligible. So $t_{31} = t_{32} = 0$, and $t_{33} = 1$. Therefore, having a regular union is an absorbing state.

Let us look at an earlier example: census tracts that can be distributed over three states. Is one of these states absorbing? Yes; it is almost always the case that once a tract becomes more than 80 percent Negro it never goes back to being all white or mixed. This is not an assumption; it is an empirical generalization. Such a statement does not mean that segregation is a one-way street. A tract might change from state 2 to state 1, though it more frequently goes the other way. But there does seem to be some sort of threshold such that when the concentration of Negroes has passed a certain point, it is irreversible. Of course, this trend must be due to certain historical conditions; it may change as attitudes toward Negroes change. But as of 1960 (the latest date for which data was available to the writer at time of writing), state 3 was absorbing.

Absorption Time. As soon as the fact that a process has at least one absorbing state has been empirically established, we can ask how long it will be before all elements end up in such a state. In our last example, we might ask how long it will be before all census tracts are all Negro. Note carefully: what is asked for here is not a *prediction* but an extrapolation. We are asking: *If* the process continues in the same manner, how long will it take for all tracts to be absorbed? A prediction would require that we assume that the process will, in fact, continue as before.

A Processual Index of Segregation. Before going into the details of how to calculate absorption time, let us ask what we could do with such a figure. First, remember that the transition matrix is based on changes that took place in the past—but *when* in the past? This time is determined by the availability of data. Census tract data are available for United States cities for the years 1940, 1950, and 1960. To establish a transition matrix we need only two dates. We could use the 1940–1950 changes to set up a matrix, M; then we could use the 1950–1960 changes to set up another matrix, M', which, of course, might be different from M. Using M we can calculate how long it would take for all tracts to go into state 3; call this figure t_1. Then we could use M' to get another time, t_2. The ratio $R = t_1/t_2$ would be a good measure of how fast the rate of segregation was changing.

If $t_1 = t_2$, then $R = 1$, indicating no change. If t_1 is less than t_2, the rate of segregation is decreasing (it is taking longer for tracts to become all Negro); if t_2 is less than t_1, the rate of segregation is speeding up. Thus R would be a measure of the "process" of segregation (unlike most indexes, which measure the amount of segregation).[4]

Calculating Absorption Time. Here we will just sketch the method and give an example. The reader is referred to Kemeny, Snell, and Thompson[5] for a more complete derivation. Let us start with a simpler illustration than that required by our example. We could have just two states: up to 80 percent Negro (state a), and more than 80 percent Negro (state b). The transition matrix would be:

$$\begin{pmatrix} p_{aa} & p_{ab} \\ 0 & 1 \end{pmatrix}$$

The entry p_{aa} is the probability that tracts will *not* go into state b. Clearly, $p_{ab} = 1 - p_{aa}$ is the probability that tracts will change state. Therefore, $1/p_{ab}$ can give us an estimate of the time required for tracts in state a to go into state b. The number $1/p_{ab}$ is called the inverse of p_{ab} and is frequently written $(p_{ab})^{-1}$.

When we are dealing with a larger number of states, the principle is the same but the arithmetic is a little more complicated. With three states, the matrix of transition probabilities is:

$$\begin{pmatrix} p_{11} & p_{12} & p_{13} \\ p_{21} & p_{22} & p_{23} \\ 0 & 0 & 1 \end{pmatrix}$$

The numbers off the main diagonal are probabilities that changes of state will occur. But we must deal with these numbers in matrix form, because the matrix as a whole determines the distribution. Here we must introduce a little more matrix algebra.

A matrix called the identity matrix I plays a role in matrix algebra similar to the role of the number 1 in ordinary algebra. The identity matrix is found by putting entries of 1 on the main diagonal of a square matrix and entries of 0 elsewhere. The 2×2 identity matrix is

$$I = \begin{pmatrix} 1 & 0 \\ 0 & 1 \end{pmatrix}$$

and the 3×3 identity matrix is

$$I = \begin{pmatrix} 1 & 0 & 0 \\ 0 & 1 & 0 \\ 0 & 0 & 1 \end{pmatrix}$$

The reader can easily form larger ones. If we multiply any square matrix, say, A, by I (a matrix of the same size), we discover that $IA = AI = A$.

We use I to define the "inverse" of a matrix. For a square matrix A, it is sometimes (but not always) possible to find another matrix, A^{-1}, such that

$$AA^{-1} = A^{-1}A = I$$

Then A^{-1} is the inverse of A.

The reader has already met a limited form of the inverse. The inverse of a permutation matrix is simply its transpose. (Try a few and see.) But in most cases calculating the inverse is a rather complicated process. Following is an outline of the method for a 2×2. Suppose that our matrix is

$$A = \begin{pmatrix} a_{11} & a_{12} \\ a_{21} & a_{22} \end{pmatrix}$$

We want to find its inverse, which we indicate by $A^{-1} = B$:

$$B = \begin{pmatrix} b_{11} & b_{12} \\ b_{21} & b_{22} \end{pmatrix}$$

By definition, $BA = I$. Because equal matrices are equal in every entry, every entry in BA can be set equal to the corresponding entry in I, and we get the following equations:

$$b_{11}a_{11} + b_{12}a_{21} = 1$$
$$b_{11}a_{12} + b_{12}a_{22} = 0$$
$$b_{21}a_{11} + b_{22}a_{21} = 0$$
$$b_{21}a_{12} + b_{22}a_{22} = 1$$

Using well-known methods for solving simultaneous equations, we get the values of entries in B in terms of entries in A:

$$b_{11} = \frac{a_{22}}{D}$$

$$b_{12} = -\frac{a_{12}}{D}$$

$$b_{21} = -\frac{a_{21}}{D}$$

$$b_{22} = \frac{a_{11}}{D}$$

where D is $a_{11}a_{22} - a_{21}a_{12}$.

Let us make up a simple illustration of the above calculations. Suppose that in 1940 there was a city with census tracts c_i distributed as follows:

$c_1, c_2, c_3, c_4, c_5, c_6$ in state 1
c_7, c_8 in state 2
c_9, c_{10} in state 3

In 1950 the same city's distribution looked like this:

c_1, c_2, c_3, c_4 in state 1
c_5, c_6, c_7 in state 2
c_8, c_9, c_{10} in state 3

and in 1960 the tracts were distributed like this:

c_1, c_7 in state 1
c_2, c_5 in state 2
$c_3, c_4, c_6, c_8, c_9, c_{10}$ in state 3

Making up the 1940–1950 transition matrix requires only counting and elementary arithmetic. The reader should verify each entry himself.

$$
\begin{aligned}
p_{11} &= \tfrac{4}{6} & p_{12} &= \tfrac{2}{6} & p_{13} &= 0 \\
p_{21} &= 0 & p_{22} &= \tfrac{1}{2} & p_{23} &= \tfrac{1}{2} \\
p_{31} &= 0 & p_{32} &= 0 & p_{33} &= 1
\end{aligned}
$$

More compactly written, the matrix would be:

$$
T_1 = \begin{pmatrix} \tfrac{4}{6} & \tfrac{2}{6} & 0 \\ 0 & \tfrac{1}{2} & \tfrac{1}{2} \\ 0 & 0 & 1 \end{pmatrix}
$$

In our earlier example we subtracted p_{aa} from 1. The analogous matrix operation is subtracting the submatrix

$$
\begin{pmatrix} \tfrac{4}{6} & \tfrac{2}{6} \\ 0 & \tfrac{1}{2} \end{pmatrix}
$$

from the identity matrix, giving us:

$$
\begin{pmatrix} \tfrac{2}{6} & -\tfrac{2}{6} \\ 0 & \tfrac{1}{2} \end{pmatrix}
$$

This matrix is now inverted by the formula given:

$$
t'_{11} = \frac{\tfrac{1}{2}}{\tfrac{1}{6} - 0} = 3
$$

$$
t'_{12} = -\frac{-\tfrac{2}{6}}{\tfrac{1}{6}} = 2
$$

$$
t'_{21} = \frac{0}{\tfrac{1}{6}} = 0
$$

$$
t'_{22} = \frac{\tfrac{2}{6}}{\tfrac{1}{6}} = 2
$$

More compactly written:

$$
\begin{pmatrix} 3 & 2 \\ 0 & 2 \end{pmatrix}
$$

The sum of these entries is 7, which is the number of time periods spent in transient states. Because each time period here is a decade, we extrapolate that on the basis of the 1940–1950 changes, in 70 years, all tracts will be more than 80 percent Negro.

Now let us make up a transition matrix based on the 1950–1960 data:

$$q_{11} = \tfrac{1}{4} \qquad q_{12} = \tfrac{1}{4} \qquad q_{13} = \tfrac{1}{2}$$
$$q_{21} = \tfrac{1}{3} \qquad q_{22} = \tfrac{1}{3} \qquad q_{23} = \tfrac{1}{3}$$
$$q_{31} = 0 \qquad q_{32} = 0 \qquad q_{33} = 1$$

In more compact form, the matrix would be:

$$\begin{pmatrix} \tfrac{1}{4} & \tfrac{1}{4} & \tfrac{1}{2} \\ \tfrac{1}{3} & \tfrac{1}{3} & \tfrac{1}{3} \\ 0 & 0 & 1 \end{pmatrix}$$

Subtracting from the identity matrix:

$$\begin{pmatrix} 1 & 0 \\ 0 & 1 \end{pmatrix} - \begin{pmatrix} \tfrac{1}{4} & \tfrac{1}{4} \\ \tfrac{1}{3} & \tfrac{1}{3} \end{pmatrix} = \begin{pmatrix} \tfrac{3}{4} & -\tfrac{1}{4} \\ -\tfrac{1}{3} & \tfrac{2}{3} \end{pmatrix}$$

Inverting these by the formula yields:

$$t_{11}' = \tfrac{8}{5}$$
$$t_{12}' = \tfrac{3}{5}$$
$$t_{21}' = \tfrac{4}{5}$$
$$t_{22}' = \tfrac{9}{5}$$

Summing these entries gives us 4.8 time periods, or 48 years.

Now, take the ratio of the first time periods to the second:

$$R = \frac{70}{48} = 1.46$$

This number is a measure of the rate at which segregation is speeding up.

Sociological Interpretation. The ratio R is a measure of the process of segregation. What we do with it after calculation depends not on our skill as mathematicians but upon our insight as sociologists. We might try to find out why segregation speeded up in a particular city, or we might look at a number of different cities and see what caused differing values of R. We might try to correlate R with degrees of social unrest, or degrees of status congruence, or amount of discrimination and so on. The author and his wife calculated ratios for a number of different cities; these R's are listed in Table 2. The reader is invited to try his hand at analyzing these results.

TABLE 2.   Segregation Indexes for Selected U. S. Cities *
1940, 1950, and 1960

CITY	t_1	t_2	R
Austin, Texas	∞	∞	1.00
Buffalo, N.Y.	∞	216	greater than 1.00
Boston, Mass.	∞	264	greater than 1.00
Cambridge, Mass.	∞	∞	1.00
Cleveland, Ohio	341	238	1.43
St. Louis, Mo.	639	125	5.11
Washington, D.C.	164	79	2.07

* The symbol ∞ is the mathematical notation for infinity. In this context, infinity means that in this time period there was no increase in the number of segregated areas. (Hence the conclusion that it would take infinitely long for all areas to become segregated.) For Buffalo and Boston, the mathematician would claim that to divide infinity by a finite number is meaningless, but in the present context it simply indicates that in the second time period some new areas did become segregated.

SOURCE: Taken from U. S. Census figures for 1940, 1950, and 1960.

The time periods are given in years. In working with data from 1940, 1950, and 1960 working with decades is actually unnecessary, because the 10s cancel out when we compute R. But if we wanted to check results with a special census conducted in, say, 1963, we would have to use years rather than just the number of time periods.

The index is not restricted to the study of segregation. Any social process where the units pass through some series of states and where there is at least one absorbing state can be analyzed with the ratio R.

nonabsorbing chains

Clearly, not every Markov chain has an absorbing state. Moreover, not every social process is destined to end up in some final state. But we can still make some useful calculations.

It is possible for a process to reach a steady state—one where the overall distribution is not changing, though individual elements may move from one state to another. For example, suppose we have a distribution vector **(4, 6)** and a transition matrix:

$$T = \begin{pmatrix} \frac{1}{2} & \frac{1}{2} \\ \frac{1}{3} & \frac{2}{3} \end{pmatrix}$$

The reader can convince himself that $dT = d$ (and therefore that $dT = dT^2 = dT^3 \ldots$). This means that the distribution is not changed during the process, no matter how long the process continues.

We can show that any transition matrix, T, having the property that some power of it has only positive entries, will have a vector, t, called the fixed point of the matrix, such that $tT = t$. Much current sociological theory is concerned with the idea of "equilibrium," which would seem to find a natural mathematical expression in this kind of Markov chain. But the reader can exercise his sociological imagination to find illustrations of equilibrium.

Exercise: We can think of voting in a party system as a Markov chain. The "states" would be the parties for which the voter casts his ballot. In the contemporary United States, the three states would be:

> State 1: Republican
> State 2: Democratic
> State 3: "independent" or "third" parties

There does not seem to be any absorbing state. By seeing how various electoral units vote in two successive elections, set up a transition matrix, and from this matrix, calculate a fixed point—the point where the number of voters switching *to* some party is balanced by the number of voters switching *away* from it.

A number of uses can be made of this fixed point. For instance, we could calculate such points for a series of elections. A dramatic change in the fixed point vector would be a measure of the appeal of a particular candidate, independent of his party. Such "appeal" might, of course, be negative. The reader might try this technique by looking at a number of counties in some area of the United States, seeing how they voted in Presidential elections since 1900, and calculating fixed point vectors. Then, on the basis of the 1950–1960 vector, he could estimate the effect of the Goldwater candidacy.

Calculating the Fixed Point. The fixed point theorem can be stated as follows. If we have a matrix, T, such that some power of T has all positive entries, then there is a vector, $t = (t_1, t_2 \ldots t_k)$, such that $tT = t$. If we take successive powers of T, then every row of T will come closer and closer to the form of t. Let us calculate the fixed point of a 2×2 matrix to illustrate this principle.

Take as the matrix

$$T = \begin{pmatrix} .9 & .1 \\ .5 & .5 \end{pmatrix}$$

(Note that this matrix has all positive entries.)

The reader should verify the following calculations:

$$T^2 = \begin{pmatrix} .86 & .14 \\ .70 & .30 \end{pmatrix}$$

$$T^3 = \begin{pmatrix} .84 & .16 \\ .81 & .22 \end{pmatrix}$$

$$T^4 = \begin{pmatrix} .83 & .17 \\ .81 & .19 \end{pmatrix}$$

By doing some more multiplication, the reader can convince himself that both rows of the matrix are coming very close to the vector **(.827, .173).** The reader can verify that this is a fixed point by multiplying it by the original T.

The generalization to three or more states is obvious and straightforward.

theory of games

This mathematical system is misleadingly titled. One might think it was concerned only with such pastimes as dice and baseball.

Actually, it is concerned with any kind of situation where the outcome of an actor's behavior depends in part on the behavior of other people, and the actors take each other's expected behavior into account when choosing their own courses of behavior. The comprehensive scope of this system would seem to make it a natural technique for describing and analyzing social behavior, and this was the hope of many sociologists when they became aware of game theory in the 1950s. But despite the fact that some social scientists (notably Shubick [6] and Rapoport [7]) are still investigating it, many others have decided that, at least in its present form, the theory of games is of very limited usefulness.

One of the difficulties is that numerical values must be given to possible outcomes of action. This problem is not too serious in economics (where the theory of games was first applied), but numbers are not easily assigned to other areas of behavior. In principle, we should be able to assign units of "utility," working perhaps in the way Homans does in his "exchange" theory.[8]

We shall return to this problem later. For the moment, let us assume that it has been solved—that is, we can assign numerical values to outcomes. If the reader wishes, he may think of the numbers as representing dollars and cents.

Zero Sum Games

There are many interaction situations where one person's loss is the other's gain, the obvious case being where the winner is paid something by the loser. If the winner's reward is $+A$, we can write the loser's cost as $-A$. Because $+A + (-A) = 0$, this is called a zero sum game. Let us represent this as a 1×1 matrix. Call the players R (for row) and C (for column). We can represent the game as

$$C$$
$$R\,(+A)$$

Because this is a zero sum game, we need only indicate R's reward $(+A)$; clearly, C's loss is $-A$.

Sometimes C has some control over his loss; he may have some alternative actions open to him. Let us call his alternatives C_1, $C_2 \ldots \ldots C_n$. For the sake of accuracy in our illustration, we will say that he has three alternatives, with respective "costs" of 3, -2, and 0. (Note that a cost of -2 means a gain of 2 points for C.) We can represent his alternatives as a row vector:

$$
\begin{array}{ccc}
C_1 & C_2 & C_3 \\
R \, (3 & -2 & 0)
\end{array}
$$

Clearly, C should always choose alternative 2. We can formalize this observation in a rule: C should always choose an outcome that is a row minimum.

Now let us go back to the case where C has only one course of action open to him. We now let R have more than one alternative, which can be called $R_1, R_2 \ldots \ldots R_m$. Say that he has three alternatives and that their outcomes are 3, 5, and -1. We can represent this situation as a column vector:

$$
\begin{array}{c}
C \\
\begin{array}{c}
R_1 \\
R_2 \\
R_3
\end{array}
\begin{pmatrix}
3 \\
5 \\
-1
\end{pmatrix}
\end{array}
$$

Clearly, R should choose the alternative that offers the largest gain (in this case it is the second). Thus we have another rule: R should always choose a column maximum.

The alternatives open to R and C are called pure strategies. The two rules can be combined to enable R to choose a strategy that will maximize his expected reward and to enable C to choose a strategy that will minimize his expected loss. The theory of games is a technique for combining the rules.

Our next step is to consider the case where R and C both have multiple strategies open to them. We can use a numerical example in which R and C are playing a game and each has two strategies. The outcomes are given in the following "game" matrix:

$$
\begin{array}{c}
\begin{array}{cc}
C_1 & C_2
\end{array} \\
\begin{array}{c}
R_1 \\
R_2
\end{array}
\begin{pmatrix}
1 & 2 \\
3 & 4
\end{pmatrix}
\end{array}
$$

(This game seems loaded, since R always wins. But this is only appearance as we shall see later.) If both R and C play their first alternatives, R wins 1 point; if both play their second alternatives, R wins 4 points and so on. Clearly, R would be foolish ever to play anything but R_2. If this conclusion is evident to R, it is also evident to C, so he would be wise always to play C_1. Note that the expected outcome is 3. This number is neither the largest possible gain for R nor the smallest possible loss for C, but it is what R can expect to gain. Note further that R's and C's decisions are in accordance with our rules. The number 3 is a column maximum because it is larger than 1; it is a row minimum because it is smaller than 4. When an outcome that is simultaneously a column maximum and a row minimum exists, we say that the game is "strictly determined."

We said the game described above seemed unfair to C because he never won anything. The following game seems more fair:

$$
\begin{array}{cc}
& C_1 \quad\ C_2 \\
\begin{array}{c} R_1 \\ R_2 \end{array} &
\begin{pmatrix} -2 & -1 \\ 0 & 1 \end{pmatrix}
\end{array}
$$

If R plays R_1, then C winds up with either 1 or 2 points. But naturally R would never play anything but his second strategy, and C would always play his first. In this case neither one wins or loses. Notice that their choice of strategies is the same as in the previous game, which should not be surprising because the two games are, actually, both the same game. The second matrix is obtained from the first by subtracting 3 from every entry. We could obtain identical games by adding or subtracting any constant so long as we did the same thing to every entry. We could also multiply every entry by a positive constant without changing the game. (This should be obvious upon making the following consideration: if we originally set up the game matrix in dollars, the choice of strategies should not change if we convert to cents, even though such a conversion multiplies every entry by 100.) We say that a game is invariant under such a transformation. But since this is true, we can, for convenience, consider only games with positive entries without loss of generality.

Not all games are strictly determined. Consider the following game:

$$
\begin{array}{cc}
& C_1 \quad C_2 \\
\begin{array}{c} R_1 \\ R_2 \end{array} &
\begin{pmatrix} 2 & 1 \\ 1 & 2 \end{pmatrix}
\end{array}
$$

No entry is simultaneously a row minimum and a column maximum. How would the game be played? If R plays R_1 then C will play C_2 to minimize his losses. When R sees this he will switch to R_2, so of course C will go to C_1 . . . . around and around. Obviously no single pure strategy will be satisfactory for either, so each will adopt a "mixed" strategy—sometimes playing one alternative, sometimes another, with a certain frequency.

If R has two strategies and he plays the first with frequency p_1 and the second with frequency $p_2 = 1 - p_1$, we can represent this pair of strategies as a distribution vector: $p = (p_1, p_2)$. Similarly, we can write the frequency with which C plays his strategies as a column vector:

$$q = \begin{pmatrix} q_1 \\ q_2 \end{pmatrix}$$

Finally, we can represent a general 2×2 game by a matrix:

$$G = \begin{pmatrix} a & b \\ c & d \end{pmatrix}$$

Now form the product pGq:

$$(p_1, p_2)G(q) = (p_1a + p_2c, p_1b + p_2d)\begin{pmatrix} q_1 \\ q_2 \end{pmatrix}$$
$$= p_1aq_1 + p_2cq_1 + p_1bq_2 + p_2dq_2$$

Note that this rather long expression is a single number; it is the "expected value of the game" for R. (Its negative would be the expected value for C, because this is a zero sum game.) Let us analyze the terms that go into it. The first term is p_1aq_1. This is the value a of that outcome for R times the probability that R plays his first alternative and that C plays his first alternative. In other words, it is the value of that outcome times the probability that that outcome in fact will occur. The other terms are analyzed in a similar manner. Thus the expected value of a game is nothing but all the various outcomes, each multiplied by the probability that it will in fact occur. Let us call this expected value E. In any particular game, neither player may get E. He may get more or less; in some games it may not even be possible to get E in a single play. For example, in tossing pennies, the expected value for each player is one-half cent. Obviously no one can get this amount on a single toss. But in the long run the expected value is what the player should average.

The expected value of the game for R is pGq. But R, in deciding what frequency to play a particular strategy (say, R_1), must consider that the frequency p_i can take on any value from 0 to 1. Moreover, C has a similar embarrassment of riches. The heart of game theory is a theorem proved by von Neumann, stating that there is always a best (optimal) strategy $p°$ for R and a best strategy for C. Strategy $p°$ is optimal in that it maximizes E for R. However, by playing $p°$, R will not necessarily get the highest possible return. If C plays something other than his optimal strategy, R might be able to get more than E. This would mean that C was acting foolishly; but it is seldom safe to bet that your opponent is a fool!

Determining the best strategy (especially when a pure strategy is not optimal) can be a complicated matter. We will not go into such a determination in this book, because the purpose here is to introduce ideas rather than specific techniques. Probably the best book to consult for methods of solution is Luce and Raiffa's *Games and Decisions*.[9]

Application to Sociology

The theory of games as a calculational device to choose strategies can be useful to planners and decision makers. Indeed, it is widely used in this *prescriptive* way. However, we are concerned with the theory of games as part of sociological theory and therefore must examine its *descriptive* utility. Can game mathematics be used to describe and explain ordinary social behavior?

We have already mentioned one problem. Because the theory of games is concerned with maximizing expected value of behavior, it is obvious that we must be able to recognize a maximum value if it occurs, and consequently we must be able to measure outcomes on at least an ordinal scale. Although such a measurement is by no means easy to make, it does not seem to present an insurmountable obstacle. People *do* measure outcomes, however subjectively (and perhaps inconsistently). Determination of the ordering of some potential outcomes should not be impossible for the sociologist.

The measurement of outcomes immediately raises another problem.

The sociologist using game technique must be very careful to specify just what is being maximized. Clearly, people do not always maximize monetary rewards. Certain norms and values modify the behavior of the most "hard-headed" individuals. To use the cliché, most people won't "sell their mothers to make a buck." But surely no fundamental problem is encountered by taking these into account when setting up a preferential ordering. People get some satisfaction from following norms, even if it is only the negative satisfaction of not being punished; this satisfaction should be in some way measurable. Of course, one must be aware of the danger of circular reasoning (saying that what in fact occurred must have been the most preferred).

These and related difficulties are essentially technical problems that may be hard to deal with but that do not indicate an inherent weakness in game theory. However, there is a more fundamental question that the sociologist must ask. Game theory purports to describe the most "rational" choice among possible alternatives. To what extent are people rational in this sense?

An analysis of the literature on the nonrational determinants of human behavior (Freud, Pareto) would be inappropriate here. The reader is at least aware that we have no a priori assurance that people choose the most rational course of behavior. We can illustrate the problem by developing the mathematics of game theory a little further.

Nonzero Sum Games

There are many interaction situations where the rewards accruing to one participant are not costs to the other. These are nonzero sum games. To take a fictitious example: A young man has recently met a girl; there is some mutual attraction. The man is thinking of asking her to attend a dance with him next weekend, but he knows she may be thinking of going out of town then. She knows he is thinking of asking her. He must decide whether to ask her or not; she must decide whether to plan to be out of town as she previously intended. The game might be represented like this:

$$\begin{array}{cc} & \text{Girl} \\ & \begin{array}{cc} \text{Stay} & \text{Go} \end{array} \\ \begin{array}{c} \text{Man} \quad \text{Ask} \\ \text{Not ask} \end{array} & \begin{pmatrix} 1,\ 1 & 0,0 \\ -1,\ -1 & 0,0 \end{pmatrix} \end{array}$$

In each cell, the first figure represents the reward (or cost) to the man; the second figure represents the reward to the girl. For example, if he asks her and she has decided to stay and accept his invitation, then both get a positive reward, set arbitrarily at 1. If she has decided to stay and he doesn't ask her, both lose out; hence -1 for each. If she plans to go, all outcomes are set at 0. (How realistic this selection of outcomes may be is irrelevant to our illustration.)

Consider the man's strategy first. We are interested only in the first entry in each cell. Each entry in the first row is equal to or better than the corresponding entry in the second row. We say row 1 "dominates" row 2. Clearly his best strategy is to ask; he has nothing to lose, whereas by not asking he has nothing to gain.

Turning to the young lady, we confine our interest to the second entry in each cell. If there was a column such that each entry in that column was equal to or larger than the corresponding entry in the second column, we would say that that column dominated the other. But this is not the case. Should she go or stay? If she knows the man's intentions (or even his evaluation of the outcomes) she can choose to stay. Otherwise, she has no basis for choice.

Notice that in a zero sum game, it is *never* advantageous for one player to let the other player know what he intends to do. But in this game, it would be better for both if each knew what the other was planning.

Rather than pursue this game further, let us turn to a game that has aroused considerable controversy.[10] It is called The Prisoners' Dilemma and can be formulated as follows: Two men have been arrested by the police in connection with a major robbery. Both men were armed when captured; therefore, they can certainly be convicted of illegal possession of firearms, which usually carries a sentence of 5 years. The police and the prisoners know that there is not enough evidence to convict either man of the robbery unless one of them confesses, so the police separate the prisoners and offer each a deal. If both confess, each man will get 10 years. But if only one confesses, the one who helped the police will get only 5 years, whereas the other will get 20. The game looks like this (negative entries indicate years "lost"):

Prisoner
No. 2

		Confess	Not Confess
Prisoner	Confess	$\begin{pmatrix} -10, -10 \\ -20, -5 \end{pmatrix}$	$\begin{pmatrix} -5, -20 \\ -5, -5 \end{pmatrix}$
No. 1	Not Confess		

Consider Prisoner No. 1. Because -10 is larger than -20 and $-5 = -5$, the "confess" row dominates the "not confess" row. Similarly, for Prisoner No. 2, the "confess" column dominates the other. Therefore, the best strategy would be for both to confess— even though the outcome would be less desirable for both than if neither were to confess. The most rational outcome is hardly the most preferred.

Clearly, the degree of trust that the prisoners have in each other has been omitted here. If one prisoner believes the other to be a "rat," then he will confess to save his own skin. But if each prisoner has faith in the other, neither will confess. Game theory cannot predict what they will do (their action is independent of what the theory says they *should* do) because it cannot take into account the nonrational factor of trust.

David Messick has come to a similar conclusion. In reporting the outcome of a study of decision-making in zero sum games, he states that "In complete accord with the previous research on the issue, the study reported here unambiguously indicates that human Ss do not behave in a manner consistent with the minimax theory. The very fact that Ss react differently to different opponents suggests that the determinants of human decision strategies in interdependent contexts are not exclusively those dealt with by the classical theory of games." [11]

The fault here does not lie with the mathematicians. If sociologists want to use game theory, they must determine the relevant factors in choosing strategies and find a way to work them into the mathematical structure. Otherwise, this suggestive mathematical theory can be of little use to the sociological theorist.

EXERCISE — CHAPTER III

Although, as indicated, game theory is not yet adequate as a descriptive technique, you might use its prescriptive abilities in sociological theory. You can try using game techniques to indicate how two persons (or two groups, or an individual and a group) ought to behave to achieve certain goals and interpret the strategies as conditions for achievement. This procedure sidesteps the question whether humans act rationally and instead focuses on the likelihood of these conditions coming about. As far as I know this possibility has not been investigated. The reader is invited to try his hand.

NOTES

1. I. Blumen, M. Kogan, and P. McCarty, *The Industrial Mobility of Labor as a Probability Process* (Ithaca, N.Y.: Cornell University Press, 1955).

2. B. P. Cohen, "A Probability Model for Conformity," in *Sociometry*, 21, No. 1 (March 1958), 69–81.

3. Murray Beauchamp, "Processual Indices of Segregation: Some Preliminary Comments," in *Behavioral Science*, 11, No. 3 (May 1966), 190–192.

4. O. D. Duncan, and B. A. Duncan, "A Methodological Analysis of Segregation Indices," in *American Sociological Review*, 20, 1955, 210–217.

5. John Kemeny, L. Snell and G. Thompson, *An Introduction to Finite Mathematics* (Englewood Cliffs, New Jersey: Prentice-Hall, 1957), 327–330.

6. M. Shubick (ed.), *Game Theory and Related Approaches to Social Behavior* (New York: Wiley, 1964).

7. Anatol Rapoport, *Fights, Games, and Debates* (Ann Arbor: University of Michigan Press, 1960).

8. George Homans, *Social Behavior: Its Elementary Forms* (New York: Harcourt, Brace & World, 1961). See especially pp. 39 ff.

9. R. Duncan Luce, and Howard Raiffa, *Games and Decisions* (New York: Wiley, 1957).

10. Anatol Rapoport, "Escape from Paradox," in *Scientific American*, July 1967, pp. 50–56.

11. David M. Messick, "Interdependent Decision Strategies in Zero-Sum Games: A Computer Controlled Study," in *Behavioral Science*, 12, No. 1 (January 1967), 33–48.

calculus and symbolic logic

Any mathematical system can be considered a formal language. However, just because a system is a "language" does not mean that we can always use the system to say what we want. In this chapter we will look at two languages that have had widespread use in other sciences but that so far have not been employed extensively by sociologists. We will see if we can learn to "read" (if not "speak") these languages, and in doing so, we will consider the possibilities of applications in our science.

The two languages are the differential calculus and symbolic logic. Because we want to gain only a "reading knowledge," the reader should not fool himself into thinking he "knows" either, merely because he understands the material in this chapter. Many introductory texts are available to the reader who wishes to go further. The purpose of this chapter is to provide motivation for doing so.

differential calculus

To the mathematician, a "calculus" is any system enabling him to calculate results. But by tradition, we frequently speak of "the calculus" to refer to the differential and integral calculus. No doubt this custom is due to the great success of this mathematical method in solving problems of physics. The conceptual framework of the physicist is probably no richer than that of the sociologist, but the physicist can use differential equations to get results, whereas the sociologist, encumbered by the clumsy manipulations of ordinary language, is much less successful in obtaining answers. The great success of calculus has unfortunately resulted in a degree of awe, and the nonmathematician too often thinks that an understanding of calculus is beyond his capabilities. This belief, of course, is non-sense. To become competent in the manipulative techniques naturally takes hard study, but an understanding of what the calculus is about and what it is used for can be quickly achieved. Several popular books cover this topic in a chapter or two, but almost all of them take their examples from physics, not sociology. Therefore, in the following discussion we will use examples that are of interest to the sociologist.

Returning to the concept of the function, the reader will recall that if we have two sets, X and Y, a function is a rule assigning a member of Y to every member of X. Suppose, for example, that X is a set of occupations and Y is a set of average incomes. We can assign to every occupation a figure representing the average income of people in that occupation. (Notice that two occupations are not prevented from having the same average income.) We could represent this relationship as $y = f(x)$, which we read as "y is a function of x." If income depends not only on occupation but also (independently) on race, we could write $y = f(x, z)$, where z would be a variable representing race. In principle any number of variables can be so related; we will consider only the case of two.

Calculus is most useful when the variables involved are continuous. (There are conditions and exceptions to this statement, but it is broadly correct.) We will see later why this fact is important. In many cases, this condition can be approximated. Time (and time-related variables like age) can be used as a continuous variable. Less obviously, income can be thought of as continuous, though the "operational" meaning of an income of $\sqrt{2}$ cents may be far from clear. Many scales can have continuous variability, but care must be exercised.

In many cases it is possible to give an explicit mathematical formula for a function. For example, the following are simple functions, each assigning a value of some set Y to every member of some set X:

$$y = 2x \qquad y = -x^2 + x + 5 \qquad y = \log x \qquad x^2 + y^2 = 25$$

In some cases we can draw a curve representing the function. To get a rough idea of what such a curve would look like, we assign a few values to x and calculate the corresponding value of y. We then use the pairs of values to place dots on a piece of graph paper, connect them, and smooth out the connecting line. For example, take the formula $y = 2x$. Assigning a few values to x, we get the following table:

x	y
0	0
1	2
2	4
3	6

These values, when plotted on graph paper, form the diagonal pattern shown in Figure 4.1.

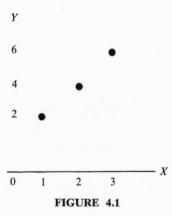

FIGURE 4.1

Connected and smoothed out, the graph yields the "picture" of $y = 2x$ shown in Figure 4.2.

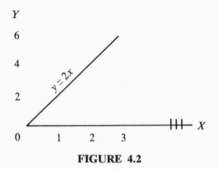

FIGURE 4.2

Take as a second example the equation $y = x^2$. Give x both positive and negative values.

X	Y
-2	$+4$
-1	$+1$
0	0
$+1$	$+1$
$+2$	$+4$

The curve representing these values is shown in Figure 4.3.

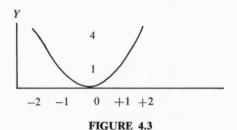

FIGURE 4.3

Finally, let us look at a more complicated curve representing the equation $y = -x^2 + 4x$. This time we will give x only positive values.

X	Y
0	0
1	3
2	4
3	3
4	0

Plotted, these values form the curve shown in Figure 4.4.

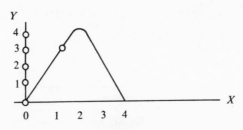

FIGURE 4.4

Sometimes we reverse the procedure by drawing the curve first and then trying to guess the equation.

Suppose, for example, that we modify a famous proposition of Homans [1] to read, "The more frequently people interact, the greater the intensity of their emotional relationship." In other words, the more often people meet, the more they like *or* dislike each other. If we represent liking by positive values of X, disliking by negative values of X, and frequency of interaction by Y, the curve would look something like the one in Figure 4.5.

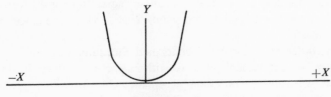

FIGURE 4.5

If we looked back at the curves we drew before, we would reach the conclusion that the actual relationship took a form like $y = x^2$ (more generally, $y = ax^2 + b$, where a and b are constants to be determined empirically).

As a second example, suppose we had a scale to measure "degree of conformity to societal norms," and we hypothesized that such conformity would be greatest in the middle classes and less in both upper and lower classes. If we used income as a (continuous) variable to measure social class, the curve representing the hypothesis would be similar to that shown in Figure 4.6.

FIGURE 4.6

We would suspect that the relationship would take the form $y = -x^2 + bx$ (where y is degree of conformity and b is a constant).

Suppose that we have determined that some curve or some mathematical formula represents the relationship between two variables. We may want to see if there is some equilibrium point. Let us take a fairly concrete example. Suppose we plan to conduct a campaign to increase acceptance of foreigners by exposing the public to some form of propaganda emphasizing certain values. Further, we know that exposure to such propaganda increases acceptance up to some point but that *more* exposure decreases acceptance. We express the relationship as $y = -x^2 + bx$. We would like to find the degree of exposure x where acceptance y is neither increasing nor decreasing—in other words, an equilibrium point. This is where the calculus becomes useful.

The differential calculus is concerned with "rate of change"—that is, how fast one variable changes with respect to another. In our example, we want to know how acceptance changes with exposure to propaganda. We can find other examples: Homans wants to know how "liking" changes with frequency of interaction; Malthus was concerned with how population increased over time. Such a rate of change is expressed by the symbol dx/dy if the variables are x and y; dp/dt if we want to know how population (P) increases with time and so on. This symbol is called the derivative. The method of calculating the derivative can be shown in a few simple instances.

The basic idea is to calculate the effect on y of a very small change in x then let that small change, denoted by Δx, "go to zero," thus giving us the rate of change at a single point. (The rate of change may be different at different points.) The phrase "go to zero" is deceptively short: it has generated multitudes of discussions, books, and papers since it was introduced. How can there be change if the amount of change has "gone to zero"? This is a fascinating question, but we have no room here to go into it adequately, so we will not go into it at all. The reader who has a taste for this kind of thing will find a discussion of "limits" in any introductory calculus text, or history of mathematics.[2]

Let us take a very simple function, $y = 4x$. If we increase x by a small amount, Δx (called the increment of x), we get $4(x + \Delta x) = 4x + 4\Delta x$. The other side of the equation will also increase by a small amount, Δy, so we get $y + \Delta y = 4x + 4\Delta x$. To see how big the increment of y is, we subtract the original equation, leaving $\Delta y = 4\Delta x$. The rate of change is given by $\Delta y / \Delta x = 4$. As the increments "go to zero," we replace them by dy/dx, which tells us that every time x increases, y increases four times as fast.

Now let us try a more complicated example, which we can also use to illustrate the method for finding equilibrium points. Suppose we found that the relationship between exposure to propaganda and acceptance of foreigners was given by $y = -x^2 + 4x$. To find the derivative, we first increment x to get

$$-(x + \Delta x)^2 + 4(x + \Delta x) = y + \Delta y$$

Expanding this equation gives us

$$-x^2 - 2x\Delta x - \Delta x^2 + 4x + 4\Delta x$$

Subtracting the original equation, we find that the increment of y is

$$\Delta y = -2x\Delta x - \Delta x^2 + 4\Delta x$$

The rate of change then is

$$\frac{\Delta y}{\Delta x} = -2x + 4 - \Delta x$$

Letting the increments "go to zero," we have

$$\frac{dy}{dx} = -2x + 4$$

We have already said that at the equilibrium point no change is taking place; that is, $dy/dx = 0$. But if the derivative is 0, it must be that $-2x + 4 = 0$. Solving the equation for x gives us 2 as an equilibrium point. Thus an exposure of 2 units (whatever they may be) would be optimal for winning acceptance of foreigners.

This method, setting the derivative equal to 0 and solving for the equilibrium point, is quite general and widely used. It is the method, for example, by which we get the equations for the "least squares" line in statistics. The following interesting application was developed by Herbert Simon.[3]

Simon's starting point was a set of propositions formulated by George Homans [4] that related some variables affecting behavior in small groups. Simon "translated" the propositions into differential equations (equations in which derivatives appear), set the derivatives equal to 0, and solved the resulting equations for equilibrium points. We will present here the variables, the propositions, and the equations; the reader should try to assure himself that the equations are in fact reasonable translations of the propositions.

Variables (all time–dependent):

$I(t)$ = intensity of interaction among members
$F(t)$ = level of friendliness among members
$A(t)$ = amount of activity carried on by members
$E(t)$ = amount of activity imposed on group by the external environment.

The postulates relating these variables can be stated verbally as follows:

1. Intensity of interaction increases with friendliness and with the amount of activity carried on within the group.
2. Group friendliness will increase if the existing level of interaction is higher than that appropriate to the existing amount of friendliness.

3. The activity carried on by the group will increase if the existing level of friendliness is higher than that appropriate to the existing amount of activity and if the amount of externally imposed activity is higher than the existing amount of activity.

These postulates can be translated into equations. The letters a_i, b_i, and c_i are constants that, in any real investigation, would have to be determined by some empirical means.

$$I(t) = a_1F(t) + a_2A(t) \tag{1}$$

$$\frac{dF(t)}{dt} = b_1I(t) - b_2F(t) \tag{2}$$

$$\frac{dA(t)}{dt} = c_1F(t) - c_2A(t) + c_3E(t) - A(t) \tag{3}$$

Equation (1) is an ordinary equation. Equations (2) and (3) are differential equations. They state how fast "friendliness" and "activity" respectively are changing as other variables change. By setting each equation equal to 0 and by using equation (1) to help solve equations (2) and (3), we can find the equilibrium levels of friendliness and activity in terms of the other variables involved.

Exercise: Try to solve for the equilibrium levels of A and F in terms of E. This problem is a little complicated but requires mathematics no more technical than ordinary algebra. If you run into problems, look at Simon's article.

This model cannot be analyzed any further without quite a bit more mathematical development, so we will leave it here. There are some excellent discussions of Simon's work in the books by Karlsson[5] and Coleman,[6] and of course Simon's original article is worth reading in entirety. The essential point to be grasped right now is the fact that verbal propositions (from Homans) can be translated into differential equations.

If such translation is now known to be possible, why has such little work been done in sociology using differential equations? The answer seems to lie in the requirements of the calculus for continuous variables. (Calculus can be used to describe variables that have discontinuities but not variables that are absolutely discontinuous. There must be "room enough" around a value of x to add an increment and then shrink it to 0.) Most variables in use in sociology are not naturally continuous. For example, a population grows by the addition of whole individuals (say 1 or 2 or 3), not by the addition of 1/2 or 1/4 of an individual. There is no real continuum of "religious affiliation" or "political preference" or "ethnic origin." In Homans' own scheme, if "interaction" is defined as a collection of separate acts and is measured by counting these acts, then $I(t)$ is not a continuous variable. Still, some derived quantities (such as birth rates or mean number of interactions per time unit) can be continuous. But many sociologists do not think that sufficient numbers of continuous variables exist to make differential equation models very useful.

We will return to this topic in the last chapter. Right now, let us discuss a different kind of "language."

symbolic logic

If calculus seems a bit strained as a language for sociology, symbolic logic at first sounds perfect. Symbolic logic is what its name implies: logic expressed by symbols. It is a form of mathematics very closely related to (and derived from) ordinary verbal reasoning. It uses natural language statements and connects them with words like "and," "or," and "implies." Since even "nonmathematical" sociologists presumably use logic in their work, the use of symbolic logic would seem the most natural way to give symbolic expression to sociological concepts and propositions. Yet looking over the literature, it is astonishing how little use has been made of symbolic logic. Even journals that encourage formal and mathematical articles, such as *Behavioral Science, Sociometry,* and *Psychometrika,* are devoid of articles using symbolic logic (with a few exceptions, such as Anderson and Moore's article on "deontic logic" [7]). Why?

Before attempting an answer, let us develop the language somewhat and try some translations into it. There are many variations and ramifications of symbolic logic; we will here develop and use just a small portion to give the flavor of the technique.

Quantifiers. Often we want to say, "For all individuals (or groups, culture traits etc.) such and such is true." We write the "for all" part of this statement by enclosing a letter in parentheses. Thus (x) would be read "for any x," whatever x may be. But if something is true only of some individuals, we write Ex, which is translated "There is an x"; that is to say, there is at least one individual for whom the statement will hold.

Propositions. To say that an individual, x, has some property, F, we write Fx. Suppose that x is a culture trait. We might use the symbolism Fx to indicate that x had a function; we might use the symbolism Px to indicate that x persists. If x and y are soldiers, we might write Ox and My to indicate that x is an officer and y is an enlisted man. (We cannot use the letter E for enlisted man—or anything else —because E is restricted to the meaning "there exists.")

Connectives. Very often we wish to make two or more statements, connecting them by "and" or "or." The symbols used are $\land$ for "and" and $\lor$ for "or." One way of translating the statement, "Every soldier is either an officer or an enlisted man," is: (x) (If Sx then $Ox \lor Mx$). In more formal English this statement would read: "If individual x is a soldier, then x is either an officer or an enlisted man." If we wish to negate a statement, we write the symbol $\sim$. For example, to say that x is not a soldier, we write $\sim Sx$.

Take the statement, "A culture trait does not persist unless it has a function." (Never mind whether you agree with it or not!) We could translate the statement as: (x) (If Px then Fx). That is, if it persists (P), a culture trait has a function. Notice that this statement is logically equivalent to: $Fx \lor \sim Px$.

Suppose we define a society as "stratified" if not all statuses within that society are equal. Let x indicate a society and Sx indicate that society x is stratified. Let p_i and p_k be two statuses in x. Then we can state our definition as follows: $Ep_i \land Ep_k (p_i \neq p_k) \lor \sim Sx$. In more formal English: There exists a position p_i, and there exists a position p_k, such that p_i is not equal to p_k, or the society is not stratified.

WARNING: The symbolism and terminology of symbolic logic are not completely standardized. Other writers might express what we have just written in different ways, so one should be rather careful in reading any work to make sure what notation and conventions are being employed. Of course, the *logic* is still the same. (A similar situation is often encountered in statistics. Occasionally a "stat" student who is having trouble with his textbook will consult a different book and become even more confused by different terminology and different notation. But the mathematics underlying statistical technique is always the same.)

As an illustration of how the sociologist can use symbolic logic in his work, let us try to formalize some statements from a theory of social stratification. Some cautions are in order before we start. First, the reader should set aside for the moment his beliefs as to the truth of the statements being made. The immediate issue is how these statements may be translated into symbolic form. Second, I do not claim to attempt a formalization of any particular theory, though my theory is obviously inspired by the famous Davis-Moore formulation. In this way I side-step the question of exactly what is important to that particular theory. Finally, I do not claim that mine is the only or even the best formalization. There is always more than one way to skin this kind of cat! But by following this formalization, the reader may be able to work out a more satisfactory one for himself. I leave this as an exercise!

I will state my theory verbally as follows: Society gives greater rewards to occupants of more important statuses so that able men will be motivated to become occupants. If able men do not occupy these important statuses, society cannot continue to exist.

To translate this theory, I will use three sets of elements. Set P will be the set of all statuses in society. Set M will consist of persons in society, and set R will be the rewards associated with the positions held by those persons. Thus p_i will indicate a certain status, m_i will indicate the occupant of that status, and r_i will be the reward given to the occupant of that status. In each set we specify a relation, G, (meaning greater than) between pairs of elements. In set P, if p_iGp_j, we interpret this statement as "Status i is more important than status j." In set M, if M_iGm_j, this statement is interpreted as "Person i is more able than person j." In set R, if r_iGr_j, this statement is interpreted as "Reward i is greater than reward j." Finally, we have a statement, Sp, which is interpreted as "Society persists."

The statement that it is necessary to have more able men in more important statuses becomes

$$(\text{If } p_iGp_j, \text{ then } m_iGm_j) \lor \sim Sp \tag{1}$$

The statement that greater rewards are sufficient motivation for more able men to accept more important positions can be written:

$$\sim (\text{If } p_iGp_j, \text{ then } r_iGr_j) \lor (\text{if } p_iGp_j, \text{ then } m_iGm_j) \qquad (2)$$

Notice that there is an important difference between statements (1) and (2). The first states a necessary condition for the persistence of society; either that condition exists or society will not persist. This condition is not sufficient—society might cease to exist for other reasons, such as a natural disaster.

On the other hand, statement (2) states a sufficient condition for the placement of able men in important positions—inequality of reward. But this statement does not rule out the possibility that other things might bring about the same result.

Combining these two observations, we might say that inequality of reward is a sufficient condition for bringing about a necessary condition for the persistence of society.

Finally, note that statement (1) depends on the statement p_iGp_j. If no position is any more important than any other, then inequality of reward is irrelevant to the persistence of society.

The converse of the last remark is that two statuses may be rewarded differently without violating statements (1) or (2), just so long as neither status is higher than the other. But there are only two ways in which this situation could occur. If two statuses are equal, there is nothing in the theory that says they have to be rewarded equally. Or if a comparison of two statuses is not possible, then one can be rewarded differently from the other. A frequent objection to the functional theory of stratification is that it cannot explain, for example, why a call girl may get more money than a congressman. But the theory as formulated here does not *have* to explain this fact, if we can say that there is no meaningful way to compare the two statuses.

Many objections can be made to the formalization of these two statements. For one thing, it does not go very far. With such a small system to work with, we cannot make any interesting deductions beyond the simple one that inequality of reward is sufficient to bring about the necessary condition for persistence of society. This deduction could have been made verbally; the symbols are essentially stenographic. A far more important objection is that statements (1) and (2) are given. The procedure would be more exciting if these statements could be derived from simpler or at least more widely accepted ideas. And it would be more convincing if Sp could be analyzed into more basic propositions (because the exact meaning of "persistence" is in doubt).

In defense of the translation, we can claim that it does state the basic ideas quite precisely, which can be quite desirable in a science like ours. If we agree or disagree with the theory as an explanation of the facts of social stratification, at least we know exactly what it is that is agreed or disagreed with. Of course, the rest of the objection is that we have not gone far enough—something that can always be said.

discussion of calculus and symbolic logic

Hopefully, the reader is now convinced that sociologically important propositions can be stated in the languages of calculus and symbolic logic. He may be less convinced that he can derive nontrivial, new propositions using this kind of mathematics, because such derivation has not really been demonstrated. (Derivation of propositions will be discussed a bit more in the last chapter.) But if this possibility is accepted, why is there such a paucity of applications in sociological literature?

Part of the problem may lie in the way mathematics has usually been taught. Two things in the usual math course tend to discourage the sociology major. One is the great attention that the mathematician pays to "fine points" that are of interest and importance to him but of less interest to many of his students. Second, the great majority of applications that are discussed relate to problems in the physical sciences. The social scientist is left to discover applications to his field by himself—a difficult business.

New ways of teaching mathematics are springing up in various places. The future undergraduate in sociology may know more mathematics than many who today have Ph.Ds. With this increasing "literacy," even sociologists who do not prefer to state their ideas mathematically may at least formulate them in such a way that they can be translated by the specialist.

Of course, the best-taught mathematics courses are of no use unless sociologists take them. The author hopes part of the function of this book will be to motivate sociology students to do so.

NOTES

1. George Homans, *The Human Group* (New York: Harcourt, Brace & World, 1950), p. 112.

2. Carl Boyer, *The History of the Calculus and Its Conceptual Development* (New York: Dover Publications, 1959). Earlier editions of this scholarly work were entitled *The Concepts of the Calculus*. There are innumerable elementary (and advanced) calculus texts that give some of the history of the subject as well as a mathematical analysis of it.

3. Herbert Simon, *Models of Man* (New York: Wiley, 1957), pp. 99–114. Read some of the footnotes in the article, relating Simon's personal communications with Homans.

4. Homans, *op. cit.*, pp. 102, 111, 112, 118, 120.

5. Georg Karlsson, *Social Mechanisms* (New York: Free Press, 1958), pp. 100–102.

6. James Coleman, "The Mathematical Study of Small Groups," in Herbert Solomon (ed.), *Mathematical Thinking in the Measurement of Behavior* (New York: Free Press, 1960), pp. 15–38.

7. A. Anderson and O. K. Moore, "The Formal Analysis of Normative Concepts," in *American Sociological Review,* 22 (January 1957), 11–17.

a few last remarks

I hope this short guided tour through a few areas of mathematical sociology has enabled the reader to decide if he wants to explore the field further. As with any guide, my choice of "points of interest" has reflected my personal taste more than it has reflected any general consensus among experts as to what is important. I think that "relational mathematics," as exemplified by graph theory, is the most natural vehicle for sociology; others place great hope in probability theory with all its ramifications (e.g., "decision theory" and statistical inference). This diversity of interests is by no means to be deplored; the more tools we have at our command, the more jobs we can perform. No one today can be expert in all branches of mathematical sociology, but it is possible to have at least some familiarity with the variety of techniques. There is no way of knowing ahead of time what kind of analysis our problems will require, so it is helpful to know what is available.

a confession

Many times in the preceding pages I have skipped or glided over certain mathematical difficulties. I felt that I could not do justice to them in a paragraph or two, and a longer exposition would divert the reader from the sociological application, which, after all, is the main focus of the book. I may have committed some sins of omission in order to achieve the greater good. But I owe the reader at least a confession.

One of the most flagrant omissions by way of oversimplification was made in Chapter IV. The derivative of a function was found by adding an increment to a value of a function and then letting the increment "go to zero." Actually, the mathematician finds what value the function approaches as the increment becomes smaller and smaller. This value is called the limit. This idea is almost impossible to convey precisely in words; even the correct mathematical formulation was not discovered until the nineteenth century. Boyer's book (see footnote 2 to Chapter IV) goes into the long, hard struggle that mathematicians went through trying to achieve a rigorous definition. Today such a definition can be found in any elementary calculus text. But "in depth" understanding of the limit concept requires considerable investigation into the notions of continuity, real numbers and so on.

The reader may have suspected some difficulties when the equation $Gf = gF$ was discussed in Chapter II. The equation was said to imply that if $F \neq G$ then $f \neq g$. But the reader, knowing that the elements in the equation were transformations, not ordinary numbers, and knowing that such transformations are not necessarily commutative, may have had difficulty seeing how the inequalities followed.

If $f = g$, then we can write $Gf = fF$. The inverse of f is f^{-1}. Multiplying both sides by this quantity we get

$$fFf^{-1} = Gff^{-1} = GI = G$$

Two transformations, F and G, related by an equation like this, are called similar. They are not, strictly speaking, equal; they are rather the same transformation from different bases. The transformations, F and G, do the same thing to the sets they are transforming.

If F is not *similar* to G, then f is not *equal* to g (because such a situation would lead to a contradiction). The illustration demonstrated that F and G are not similar because they do different things to the sets they transform. (F could not be made equal to G by a change of base.)

Some of my other sins are minor. I used the inverses of matrices and mentioned briefly that not all matrices have inverses. Perhaps I should have stated the conditions under which inverses exist. But this statement can be found in any standard algebra text. I also played fast and loose with the notion of "continuity" without giving it a rigorous definition. But I think the intuitive concept was sufficient for the purpose.

an evasion

Occasionally I used the phrase "it can be shown." My only excuse was lack of space in which to develop the requisite mathematics. I use the same excuse for a more serious evasion. In Chapter IV, I showed how some sociological propositions could be translated into mathematical form—and left it at that. Surely the most interesting part is what is done *after* the translation is made. (Moreover, in presenting Herbert Simon's model of Homans I gave only the linear form, which is terribly restricted.) After all, to show that propositions can be translated into mathematics is no more impressive than showing that they can be translated into French or Chinese. I hope the reader realizes that further manipulation is possible but that to understand it he would need more mathematical background than I had assumed him to possess.

a prediction

In 1964 James Coleman's masterful *Introduction to Mathematical Sociology* was published. This work will remain a landmark and will be the standard reference for some time. But I predict that an even more important book will be published fairly soon. It will be entitled (or subtitled) *A Mathematical Introduction to Sociology*. The contents page will be similar to a present-day introductory text, but the concepts will be defined, developed, and related by mathematical formulas.

A Mathematical Introduction to Sociology cannot be written today (1970). But it is possible, today, to teach a sociology course using mathematical formulations. (Whether it is *desirable* to teach a course in this way may be open to question; whether it is *possible* is not.) To illustrate this fact, I will use concepts from the book you are now reading.

The chapters in this book are arranged by mathematical techniques rather than by sociological concepts. I did this for pedagogical reasons. I expected the reader to have more trouble with the mathematics than with the sociology, so sustained presentation of a mathematical topic seemed more desirable than systematic disquisition of sociological theory. Below I have listed some topics that are normally covered in ordinary sociology courses, and chapters in this book where these topics are "mathematicized."

Sociological Topic	Related Mathematical Formulation
Status	Status in formal organizations—Chapter I
	Power structures, status congruence—Chapter II
Interaction	Formalization of Homans—Chapter IV
	Game theory—Chapter III
Groups	Cliques, balance—Chapter II
	Communication networks—Chapter I
Cohesion and deviance	Durkheim and Merton—Chapter I
Stratification	Formalization of stratification theory—Chapter IV
Social structure	Definition of structure and isomorphism—Chapter II
Political institutions	Harary's structure theorem—Chapter II
Urban sociology	Index of segregation—Chapter III

Many other topics have been subjected to mathematical analysis but have not been included in this book: kinship structures, diffusion of information, epidemiology, social mobility and so on. All would be relevant to courses in sociology. On the other hand, there is no subject that has been completely developed on a mathematical basis, in the sense, say, that mechanics is developed mathematically in physics. That is why *A Mathematical Introduction to Sociology* cannot be written today.

a speculation

Though the term is not very popular today, "social physics" has an old and honored history as an approach to the study of human social behavior. To many thinkers there is something very appealing about the idea that people's actions could be described as precisely as the movements of physical objects like stars or billiard balls. (To others, of course, the idea is appalling.) Physics has its greatest success in describing relatively isolated systems, like binary stars or balls rolling down inclined planes. When dealing with terribly complicated systems (for example, the world's weather), mathematics is often unable to give determinate solutions or gives such solutions only at the cost of extremely simplified assumptions. The physicist can often deal with such problems by the use of probability theory. Thus in studying the behavior of a gas, equations specifying what is happening to each molecule would be impossible to write, but the aggregate behavior of these molecules can be described by "statistical mechanics," wherein assumptions can be made about the distribution of energy.

Human societies are extremely complicated systems. Furthermore, no group and almost no society can be considered an isolated system—the determinants of behavior may be distributed in a very complicated manner, there may be feedback processes and so on. This extreme complication makes classical mathematics (so successful in Newtonian mechanics) largely inapplicable in sociology. But human populations unquestionably do exhibit statistical regularities, and relational patterns can be abstracted. I think it is quite possible that a kind of statistical mechanics, using relational constraints, may indeed be developed to provide a theory of social behavior. But further advances in both mathematics and sociology will be necessary before this development can be brought about.

concluding comment

The science of sociology is going through a period of rapid evolution. In almost every area, great advances are being made in the collection of facts, in the techniques of measurement, and in theoretical understanding. As a precise language and a unifying system of logic, mathematical sociology can play a vital role in this progress.

appendix on summation signs

A very useful symbolism is used to indicate the sum of a collection of numbers. Though this symbolism is employed extensively in mathematics and statistics, explicit directions for its use are for some reason seldom given. Summation involves nothing more complicated than elementary arithmetic, but the beginner in mathematics is often confused by it, so a "summary on summation" may be useful.

The symbol used is the Greek letter sigma: Σ. Suppose you have a collection of numbers: $X_1, X_2 \ldots X_n$. The numbers $1, 2, \ldots n$ are called subscripts. They have no numerical significance; they are just labels that have been put on different values of X. The formula $\sum_{i=1}^{n} X_i$ means simply $X_1 + X_2 + \ldots . X_n$. Suppose, for example, that $X_1 = 3$, $X_2 = 4$, and $X_3 = 7$. Then

$$\sum_{i=1}^{n} X_i = X_1 + X_2 + X_3 = 3 + 4 + 7 = 14.$$

In principle we should always write n and i above and below the summation sign, but in practice they are often omitted as long as there is no danger of confusion.

You may verify the following rules by using the laws of ordinary arithmetic. The letter k is any constant (a number whose magnitude does not change).

$$\Sigma kX_i = kX_1 + kX_2 + \cdots kX_n = k\Sigma X_i \tag{1}$$

$$\Sigma k = nk \tag{2}$$

$$\Sigma(X + Y - Z) = \Sigma X + \Sigma Y - \Sigma Z \tag{3}$$

Note that for typographical convenience we have omitted the subscripts on X, Y, and Z. This omission should cause no confusion. In this and subsequent rules and examples, it is understood that X is really X_i.

In general, ΣX^2 is *not* equal to $(\Sigma X)^2$.

$$\Sigma X^2 = X_1^2 + X_2^2 + \cdots \cdot X_n^2 \tag{4}$$

In general, ΣXY is *not* equal to $(\Sigma X)(\Sigma Y)$.

$$\Sigma XY = X_1Y_1 + X_2Y_2 + \cdots \cdots X_nY_n \tag{5}$$

In working through the following example, you might try to note exactly which of the above rules are being applied in every step.
Example: Show that

$$\Sigma(X - \bar{X})^2 = \Sigma X^2 - \frac{(\Sigma X)^2}{N}$$

where $\bar{X}$ is the arithmetic mean.

Note first that the mean is a constant and that, by definition,

$$\bar{X} = \frac{(\Sigma X)}{N}$$

$$\Sigma(X - \bar{X})^2 = \Sigma(X^2 - 2X\bar{X} + \bar{X}^2) = \Sigma X^2 - 2\bar{X}\Sigma X + N\bar{X}^2$$

Substituting for $\bar{X}$ gives us

$$\Sigma X^2 - 2\frac{\Sigma X}{N}(\Sigma X) + \frac{N(\Sigma X)^2}{N^2} = \Sigma X^2 - 2\frac{(\Sigma X)^2}{n} + \frac{(\Sigma X)^2}{N}$$

Adding the two last terms gives us

$$\Sigma(X - \bar{X})^2 = \Sigma X^2 - \frac{(\Sigma X)^2}{N}$$

Therefore, we can use the right-hand side of the equation, which is better suited for computation.

centrality index

In Chapter I the problem of characterizing the "pattern" of a communication network was discussed. One measurement we can make for each point (participant) in such a network is its "centrality." The centrality of a point is inversely proportional to the sum of the distances from other points and directly proportional to the number of other points. If we write d_{ij} to mean the distance of point i from point j and if there are n points altogether (including points i and j), then the centrality of point i is given by

$$\frac{n-1}{\left(\sum_{j}^{n} d_{ij}\right)}$$

If point i is in direct contact with every other point (with every point j), then its centrality is 1. Otherwise it is less than 1.

If we want to find the average centrality of points in the network, we add the centralities of all points and divide by n. Show that the average centrality is expressed by

$$\frac{(n-1)}{n} \sum_{i} \frac{1}{\sum_{j} d_{ij}}$$

annotated bibliography

In this quite incomplete bibliography I have listed some books that I feel may be useful to the sociologist who wishes to acquire further competence in the use of mathematics. I have tried to indicate how difficult I think these books may be to the novice. In this evaluation, of course, I may sometimes be unduly pessimistic or optimistic. The separation into "mathematical sociology" and "mathematics" is somewhat arbitrary, because many of the "mathematics" books have applications suggested to social science and some of the "sociology" books go quite deeply into mathematics.

Special Category
Kemeny, John, L. Snell, and G. Thompson. *An Introduction to Finite Mathematics.* Englewood Cliffs, N.J.: Prentice-Hall, 1957. This book (and later editions of it) constitutes the best reference to a wide field of mathematical techniques useful to the sociologist. Each chapter contains applications and examples from sociology and related sciences. The book is highly recommended to the beginner and also to the reader with some training in "classical" mathematics.

Mathematical Sociology

1. Berger, J., B. Cohen, J. L. Snell, and M. Zelditch, Jr. *Types of Formalization in Small-Group Research*. Boston: Houghton Mifflin, 1962. This book is an examination of three models that are useful to sociologists. It is a very lucid exposition of both mathematical principles and applications that contains a good annotated bibliography.

2. Coleman, James. *Introduction to Mathematical Sociology*. New York: Free Press, 1964. Without doubt, this book is the most comprehensive yet to be published in this field. Many parts are quite difficult, but the first chapter and many of the introductory sections of later chapters can be read profitably by any interested sociologist. The shelf of any serious mathematical sociologist must contain a copy.

3. Coleman, James. *Models of Change and Response Uncertainty*. Englewood Cliffs, N.J.: Prentice-Hall, 1964. This book is part of the Prentice-Hall series on mathematical analysis of social behavior, consisting of rather specialized monographs. I would not rate them very high on exposition, but the treatment of the topics is highly competent.

4. Flament, Claude. *Applications of Graph Theory to Group Structure*. Englewood Cliffs, N.J.: Prentice-Hall, 1963. Part of the Prentice-Hall series on mathematical analysis of social behavior.

5. Karlsson, Georg. *Social Mechanisms*. New York: Free Press, 1958. This volume covers a wide variety of models and attempts to integrate the mathematical aspects with the sociological investigations related to them. It is a very useful work and one that is not beyond the comprehension of most students.

6. Kemeny, John, and Laurie Snell. *Mathematical Models in the Social Sciences*. Boston: Ginn, 1962. Like the preceding, this book examines some social science models; it assumes a fairly high level of competence in math.

7. Rashevsky, Nicolas. *Mathematical Biology of Social Behavior*. Chicago: University of Chicago Press, 1951. The author makes a very ambitious attempt to explain social behavior on the basis of biological principles. One can question whether Rashevsky's mathematics really implies what he says it does. Nevertheless, his theories are worth looking into. Rashevsky is the author of another book entitled *Mathematical Theory of Human Relations* (Bloomington, Ind.: Principia Press, 1948) which I have never been able to obtain.

8. Simon, Herbert. *Models of Man*. New York: Wiley, 1957. This collection of essays constitutes one of the best efforts to discuss meaningful social science problems from a mathematical point of view. Sociologists most likely will be especially interested in Section II ("Social Processes"); more recently there has been an interest in Simon's essays on causality in Section I.

9. White, Harrison. *An Anatomy of Kinship*. Englewood Cliffs, N.J.: Prentice-Hall, 1963. Part of the Prentice-Hall series on mathematical analysis of social behavior.

The following books are collections of papers. I will not attempt to comment extensively on them. All are worth at least browsing through; some of the articles may serve as starting points for further investigations.

1. Criswell, Joan, Herbert Solomon, and Patrick Suppes (eds.). *Mathematical Methods in Small Group Processes*. Stanford, Calif.: Stanford University Press, 1962. Very good essays, closely tied to sociology and psychology. Not easy reading but worth the effort.
2. Machol, Robert (ed.). *Information and Decision Processes*. New York: McGraw-Hill, 1960. Fairly technical.
3. Massarik, Fred, and Philburn Ratoosh. *Mathematical Explorations in Behavioral Science*. Homewood, Ill.: Richard D. Irwin, 1965. High-powered mathematics to treat what I consider rather trivial problems (but others may not agree with this opinion).
4. Thrall, R. M., C. H. Coombs, and R. L. Davis (eds.). *Decision Processes*. New York: Wiley, 1954. Quite a bit on game theory. Chapter II gives a good exposition of the nature of mathematical models.

Graph Theory

A few years ago there were no books in English on graph theory; now there is a small library of them. Numbers 1, 3, and 4 below have definite application to sociology.

1. Busacker, Robert, and Thomas Saaty. *Finite Graphs and Networks*. New York: McGraw-Hill, 1965. A little bit tougher than the other books. Applications to sociology not extensive, but the ones given are interesting.
2. Grossman, Israel, and Wilhelm Magnus. *Groups and Their Graphs*. New York: Random House, 1965. Part of New Mathematical Library series. Aimed at high school students, but can be read with profit by college professors. Other books in this paperback series might also be of interest.
3. Harary, Frank, and Robert Norman. *Graph Theory as a Mathematical Model in Social Science*. Ann Arbor: University of Michigan Press, 1953. Only 45 pages long, but good as far as it goes. Could well serve as an introduction. Can be read by a student with minimal background in mathematics.
4. ———, and Dorwin Cartwright. *Structural Models*. New York: Wiley, 1965. The definitive book on directed graphs. Can be read by anyone willing to work a little.
5. Ore, Oystein. *Graphs and Their Uses*. New York: Random House, 1963. Part of New Mathematical Library Series.
6. ———. *Theory of Graphs*. Providence, R.I.: American Mathematical Society, 1962. The definitive book on graphs as a mathematical discipline.

Mathematics

1. Luce, R. Duncan, and Howard Raiffa. *Games and Decisions*. New York: Wiley, 1958. Not everyone agrees with me, but I think this is

the best book on game theory for the nonmathematician. Can be read by anyone willing to work.

2. Feller, William. *An Introduction to Probability Theory and Its Applications.* New York: Wiley, 1950. Definitely mathematical, but accessible to interested readers.
3. Kasner, Edward, and James Newman. *Mathematics and the Imagination.* New York: Simon and Shuster, 1964. Popularly written, but quite a serious book; can be read by anyone. Contains an especially good elementary chapter on the calculus.
4. Sutton, O. G. *Mathematics in Action.* New York: Harper & Row: 1960. Written in a popular style, but not really easy. Explains quite well how mathematics is applied in physics.
5. Whitehead, A. N. *Introduction to Mathematics.* New York: Oxford University Press, 1959. There are many editions of this fine book. Whitehead is one of the world's great mathematicians and a superb writer. The book really gives the flavor of mathematical thinking.

index

index